THE Lean Enterprise

MEMORY JOGGER™

Desktop Guide

**Create Value
and
Eliminate Waste
throughout
Your
Company**

Richard L. MacInnes
Net Results Inc.

First Edition
GOAL/QPC

The Lean Enterprise Memory Jogger™

Desktop Guide
© 2002 by GOAL/QPC
All rights reserved.

Cathy Kingery, *Editor*
Carolann Scherer, *Graphics*
Michele Kierstead, *Cover Design, Icons, Layout*
Bob Page, *Project Manager, GOAL/QPC*
Julie MacInnes, *Project Manager, Net Results Inc.*
Brian Wiley, *Project Contributor, Net Results Inc.*

GOAL/QPC

12B Manor Parkway, Salem, NH 03079-2862
800-643-4316 **or** 603-890-8800
Fax: 603-870-9122
E-mail: service@goalqpc.com
Web site: www.goalqpc.com

Printed in the United States of America

First Edition   10 9 8 7 6 5 4 3 2

ISBN 1-57681-062-3 (spiral binding)
ISBN 1-57681-057-7 (perfect binding)

Acknowledgments

Our sincere thanks to the people and organizations who reviewed draft versions of *The Lean Enterprise Memory Jogger*™ and offered suggestions and encouragement. Their participation in the development process assured us that the tools and methods described in this book are relevant and appropriate for all associates to use in their quest to achieve a truly lean enterprise.

Judy Butler
Bradford Company

Alan Cash
Northrop Grumman

Bill Coleman
Brown-Forman Corporation

Thomas A. Faust
Freudenberg-NOK

Gene Fornaro, P.E.
Margaret O'Brien
Deborah Porto
North Carolina State University IES

Michael George
Zeochem LLC

Todd Hermetz
Hexcel

Ron Hicks
Lantech Inc.

Douglas P. Knudtson
Brady Corporation

Jay Patel
Quality & Productivity Solutions Inc.

Kim W. Simpson
Nypro Inc.

Donald L. Smith
Technology Infusion

Kristi Spittler-Brown
Wal-Mart

Foreword

In today's highly competitive market, there is an intense drive to ensure that an organization's operations are as productive as possible. The benefits that result from becoming a "lean" organization include the freeing up of capital, the reduction of inventory exposure during periods of slowdown, and the ability to qualify as a preferred supplier.

The tools and methods outlined in this book for optimizing resources, streamlining operations, and eliminating waste had their origins in manufacturing. Experience, however, has shown that these methods are applicable everywhere. For this reason, we have named this book *The Lean Enterprise Memory Jogger*™.

We believe this book will enable associates at all levels to quickly learn and begin applying the most commonly used tools for creating value and eliminating waste.

We wish you well.

Bob Page
Director, Product Development
GOAL/QPC

Table of Contents

Chapter 1
Introduction

What is a lean enterprise?

Many companies today are becoming lean enterprises by replacing their outdated mass-production systems with lean systems to improve quality, eliminate waste, and reduce delays and total costs.

A lean system emphasizes the prevention of waste: any extra time, labor, or material spent producing a product or service that doesn't add value to it. A lean system's unique tools, techniques, and methods can help your organization reduce costs, achieve just-in-time delivery, and shorten lead times.

A lean enterprise fosters a company culture in which all employees continually improve their skill levels and production processes. And because lean systems are customer focused and driven, a lean enterprise's products and services are created and delivered in the right amounts, to the right location, at the right time, and in the right condition. Products and services are produced only for a specific customer order rather than being added to an inventory.

A lean system allows production of a wide variety of products or services, efficient and rapid changeover among them as needed, efficient response to fluctuating demand, and increased quality.

How to use this book

This book will explain what you need to know to transform your organization into a lean enterprise. The specific information you will learn includes the following:

- Concepts and definitions you need to know
- Skills you need to develop
- Tools you need to use
- Steps you need to take

This information will help you and your team work together systematically toward your lean-enterprise goals.

What do the icons mean?

Topics of special interest to engineering staff or team leaders are marked with this icon. Operators may choose to skip these sections.

 Topics that are best addressed by an entire team working together are marked with this icon.

Chapter 2
The Goals of the Lean Enterprise

Your organization can apply lean methods and techniques to your product-production and business processes to deliver better value to your customers. A lean initiative has four main goals:

Goal #1: Improve quality.

Quality is the ability of your products or services to conform to your customers' wants and needs (also known as expectations and requirements). Product and service quality is the primary way a company stays competitive in the marketplace.

Goal #2: Eliminate waste.

Waste is any activity that takes up time, resources, or space but does not add value to a product or service. An activity adds value when it transforms or shapes raw material or information to meet your customers' requirements. Some activities, such as moving materials during product production, are necessary but do not add value. A lean organization's primary goal is to deliver quality products and services the first time and every time. As a lean enterprise, you accomplish this by eliminating all activities that are waste and then targeting areas that are necessary but do not add value.

Goal #3: Reduce lead time.

Lead time is the total time it takes to complete a series of tasks within a process. Some examples are the period between the receipt of a sales order and the time the customer's payment is received, the time it takes to transform raw materials into finished goods, and the time it takes to introduce new products after they are first designed. By reducing lead time, a lean enterprise can quickly respond to changes in customer demand while improving its return on investment, or ROI (see Glossary).

Goal #4: Reduce total costs.

Total costs are the direct and indirect costs associated with production of a product or service. Your company must continually balance its products' and services' prices and its operating costs to succeed. When either its prices or its operating costs are too high, your company can lose market share or profits. To reduce its total costs, a lean enterprise must eliminate waste and reduce lead times.

Why are these goals important?

- Implementing lean tools and techniques will enable your company to meet its customers' demand for a quality product or service at the time they need it and for a price they are willing to pay.

- Lean production methods create business and manufacturing processes that are agile and efficient.

- Lean practices will help your company manage its total costs and provide a fair ROI to its stakeholders.

Goal #1: Improve Quality

Quality improvement begins with an understanding of your customers' expectations and requirements. Once you know what your customers want and need, you can then design processes that will enable you to provide quality products or services that will meet their expectations and requirements. In a lean enterprise, quality decisions are made every day by all employees.

How to do it LEADER

1. Begin your quality-improvement activities by understanding your customers' expectations and requirements. Tools such as quality function deployment (see Glossary) are helpful ways to better understand what your customers want and need.

2. Review the characteristics of your service or product design to see if they meet your customers' wants and needs.

3. Review your processes and process metrics to see if they are capable of producing products or services that satisfy your customers.

4. Identify areas where errors can create defects in your products or services.

5. Conduct problem-solving activities to identify the root cause(s) of errors.

6. Apply error-proofing techniques to a process to prevent defects from occurring. You might need to change either your product/service or your production/business process to do this.

7. Establish performance metrics to evaluate your solution's effectiveness.

Goal #2: Eliminate Waste

To eliminate waste, begin by imagining a perfect operation in which the following conditions exist:

- Products or services are produced only to fill a customer order—not to be added to inventory.

- There is immediate response to customer needs.

- There are zero product defects and inventory.

- Delivery to the customer is instantaneous.

By imagining a perfect operation like this, you will begin to see how much waste there is hidden in your company. Using lean initiatives will enable you to eliminate waste and get closer to a perfect operation.

The seven types of waste

As you use the tools and techniques of lean production, you will work to eliminate seven types of waste, which are defined below:

- **Overproduction**. The worst type of waste, overproduction occurs when operations continue after they should have stopped. The results of overproduction are 1) products being produced in excess quantities and 2) products being made before your customers need them.

- **Waiting.** Also known as *queuing*, this term refers to the periods of inactivity in a downstream process that occur because an upstream activity does not deliver on time. Idle downstream resources are then often used in activities that either don't add value or, worse, result in overproduction.

- **Transport.** This is the unnecessary movement of materials, such as work-in-progress (WIP) materials being transported from one operation to another. Ideally, transport should be minimized for two reasons: 1) it adds time to the process during which no value-added activity is being performed, and 2) goods can be damaged during transport.

- **Extra Processing.** This term refers to extra operations, such as rework, reprocessing, handling, and storage, that occur because of defects, overproduction, and too much or too little inventory. Another example of extra processing is when an inside salesperson must obtain customer information that should have been obtained by the outside salesperson handling the account. It is more efficient to complete a process correctly the first time instead of making time to do it over again to correct errors.

- **Inventory**. This refers to any excess inventory that is not directly required for your current customer orders. It includes excess raw materials, WIP, and finished goods. Keeping an inventory requires a company to find space to store it until the company finds customers to buy it. Excess inventory also includes marketing materials that are not mailed and repair parts that are never used.

- **Motion.** This term refers to the extra steps taken by employees and equipment to accommodate inefficient process layout, defects (see the section below), reprocessing, overproduction, and too little or too much inventory. Like transport, motion takes time and adds no value to your product or service. An example is an equipment operator's having to walk back and forth to retrieve materials that are not stored in the immediate work area.

- **Defects**. These are products or aspects of your service that do not conform to specification or to your customers' expectations, thus causing customer dissatisfaction. Defects have hidden costs, incurred by product returns, dispute resolution, and lost sales. Defects can occur in administrative processes when incorrect information is listed on a form.

Tip As you begin your lean initiative, concentrate first on overproduction, which is often a company's biggest area of waste. It can also hide other production-related waste. As your lean initiative progresses, your company will become able to use its assets for producing products or services to customer orders instead of to inventory.

How to do it LEADER

1. Begin your team-based waste-reduction activities by identifying a product or operation that is inefficient.

2. Identify associated processes that perform poorly or need performance improvement. If appropriate, select the operation in your organization with the lowest production output as a starting point for your waste-reduction activities.

3. Begin by creating a value stream map for the operation you are reviewing. (See chapter 3, "Mapping the Value Stream," for details.)

4. Review the value stream map to identify the location, magnitude, and frequency of the seven types of waste associated with this operation.

5. Establish metrics for identifying the magnitude and frequency of waste associated with this operation. (See chapter 11, "Lean Metrics," for details.)

6. Begin your problem-solving efforts by using lean principles to reduce or eliminate the waste.

7. Periodically review the metrics you have identified to continue eliminating waste associated with this operation.

8. Repeat this process with other inefficient operations in your organization.

Goal #3: Reduce Lead Time

Reducing *lead time*, the time needed to complete an activity from start to finish, is one of the most effective ways to reduce waste and lower total costs. Lead time can be broken down into three basic components:

1. **Cycle time.** This is the time it takes to complete the

tasks required for a single work process, such as producing a part or completing a sales order.

2. **Batch delay.** This is the time a service operation or product unit waits while other operations or units in the lot, or batch, are completed or processed. Examples are the period of time the first machined part in a batch must wait until the last part in the batch is machined, or the time the first sales order of the day must wait until all the sales orders for that day are completed and entered into the system.

3. **Process delay.** This is the time that batches must wait after one operation ends until the next one begins. Examples are the time a machined part is stored until it is used by the next operation, or the time a sales order waits until it is approved by the office manager.

As you think about places where you can reduce lead time in your product production or business process, consider the following areas:

- Engineering design and releases
- Order entry
- Production planning
- Purchasing
- Order fulfillment
- Receiving
- Production
- Inspection/rework
- Packaging
- Shipping
- Invoicing and payment collection

Below is a list of possible lead-time solutions to consider and their goals. They are divided into three categories: product design, manufacturing, and supply.

Product design

- Product rationalization. This involves simplifying your product line or range of services by reducing the number of features or variations in your products or services to align more directly with your customers' wants and needs.

Manufacturing

- Process simulations. These enable you to model your work processes to reveal waste and test the effects of proposed changes.

- Delayed product configuration. This means waiting until the end of your production cycle to configure or customize individual products.

- One-piece, or continuous, flow of products and information. This enables you to eliminate both batch and process delays.

- Technology (i.e., hardware and software) solutions. These enable you to reduce cycle time and eliminate errors.

- Quick changeover. This involves making product/service batch sizes as small as possible, enabling you to build to customer order.

- Work process standardization. This means identifying wasteful process steps and then standardizing "best practices" to eliminate them.

Supply

- Demand/supply–chain analysis. This reveals wasteful logistical practices both upstream and downstream in your demand/supply chain. It often reveals excess inventories being held by your customers, your organization, and/or your suppliers due to long manufacturing lead times that result in overproduction. Freight analysis sometimes reveals that overproduction occurs in an effort to obtain freight discounts. However, these discounts do not necessarily offset the costs of carrying excess inventory.

How to do it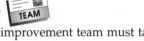

The steps your improvement team must take to reduce lead time are similar to the ones you take to eliminate waste.

1. Begin your team-based lead-time-reduction activities by creating a value stream map for the business process you are targeting. (See chapter 3, "Mapping the Value Stream," for details.)

2. Calculate the time required for the value-added steps of the process.

3. Review the value stream map to identify where you can reduce lead time. Brainstorm ways to make the total lead time equal the time required for the value-added steps that you calculated in step 2.

4. Determine what constraints exist in the process and develop a plan to either eliminate them or manage them more efficiently.

5. Establish metrics to identify the location, duration, and frequency of lead times within the process. (See chapter 11, "Lean Metrics," for details.)

6. Once you have established a plan for improving the process, measure the improvement.

7. Repeat this process for other inefficient operations in your organization.

Goal #4: Reduce Total Costs

What is it?

For cost management to be successful, everyone in your organization must contribute to the effort. When you implement a process to reduce total costs, your goal is to spend money wisely to produce your company's products or services.

To minimize the cost of its operations, a lean enterprise must produce only to customer demand. It's a mistake to maximize the use of your production equipment only to create overproduction, which increases your company's storage needs and inventory costs.

Before you can identify opportunities to reduce costs, your team should have some understanding of the way that your company tracks and allocates costs and then uses this information to make business decisions.

A company cost structure usually includes variable and fixed costs, which are explained below:

- **Variable costs.** These are the costs of doing business. These costs increase as your company makes each additional product or delivers each additional service. In manufacturing operations, variable costs include the cost of raw materials.

- **Fixed costs**. These are the costs of being in business. These costs include product design, advertising, and overhead. They remain fairly constant, even when your company makes more products or delivers more services.

Cost-Reduction Methods

Use one or more of the methods listed on the next page to identify places to reduce the costs related to your company's current processes or products/services.

These methods are useful for analyzing and allocating costs during the new-product-design process.

- **Target Pricing**. This involves considering your costs, customers, and competition when determining how much to charge for your new product or service. It's important to remember that pricing has an impact on your sales volumes, and thus your production volumes. The rise and fall of production volumes impact both the variable and fixed costs of the product—and ultimately how profitable it will be for your company.

- **Target Costing.** This involves determining the cost at which a future product or service must be produced so that it can generate the desired profits. Target costing is broken down into three main components, which enables designers to break down cost factors by product or service, components, and internal and external operations.

- **Value Engineering.** This is a systematic examination of product cost factors, taking into account the target quality and reliability standards, as well as the price. Value engineering studies assign cost factors by taking into account what the product or service does to meet customer wants and needs. These studies also estimate the relative value of each function over the product's or service's life cycle.

The following techniques are useful for analyzing and improving the cost of your organization's operations.

- **Activity-based costing (ABC)**. ABC systems allocate direct and indirect (i.e, support) expenses—first to activities and processes, and then to products, services, and customers. For example, your company might want to know what percentage of its engineering and procurement costs should be allocated to product families to determine product-contribution margin. In addition, you can do indirect cost allocations for each customer account, which enables you to do a customer-profitability analysis.

- **Kaizen (i.e., continuous improvement) costing**. This focuses on cost-reduction activities (particularly waste reduction and lead-time reduction) in the production process of your company's existing products or services.

- **Cost maintenance**. This monitors how well your company's operations adhere to cost standards set by the engineering, operations, finance, or accounting departments after they conduct target-costing and kaizen-costing activities.

How to do it LEADER

1. Decide whether your cost-improvement efforts will begin with new or existing product lines.

2. If new products or services are the focus of your improvement efforts, techniques to consider using are target pricing, target costing, and value engineering.

3. If existing products or services are your focus, begin by reviewing your company's high-cost products and processes. Apply ABC, Kaizen costing, and cost maintenance to assist your cost-improvement initiatives.

    Tip If your product-production process is inherently costly, first consider applying the lean-manufacturing techniques identified in this book. Then focus your efforts on reducing total costs. This typically involves company-wide participation.

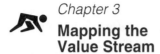

Chapter 3

Mapping the Value Stream

What is a value stream?

The term *value stream* refers to all the activities your company must do to design, order, produce, and deliver its products or services to customers. A value stream has three main parts:

- The flow of materials, from receipt from suppliers to delivery to customers.

- The transformation of raw materials into finished goods.

- The flow of information that supports and directs both the flow of materials and the transformation of raw materials into finished goods.

There are often several value streams operating within a company; value streams can also involve more than one company.

What is a value stream map, and what does it do?

A *value stream map* uses simple graphics or icons to show the sequence and movement of information, materials, and actions in your company's value stream.

It helps employees understand how the separate parts of their company's value stream combine to create products or services.

Why use it?

A value stream map is the first step your company should take in creating an overall lean-initiative plan. A lean initiative begins with agreement among employees on the current state of your organization. Developing a visual map of the value stream allows everyone to fully understand and agree on how value is produced and where waste occurs. Creating a value stream map also provides the following benefits:

- Highlighting the connections among activities and information and material flow that impact the lead time of your value stream.

- Helping employees understand your company's entire value stream rather than just a single function of it.

- Improving the decision-making process of all work teams by helping team members to understand and accept your company's current practices and future plans.

- Creating a common language and understanding among employees through the use of standard value-stream-mapping symbols.

- Allowing you to separate value-added activities (see Glossary) from non-value-added activities and then measure their lead time.

- Providing a way for employees to easily identify and eliminate areas of waste.

What areas should I focus on to create a value stream map?

To effectively create a value stream map for your company's manufacturing or business processes, you should focus on the following areas:

- The flow of information—from the receipt of a sales order or production data all the way through the engineering, production, control, purchasing, production, shipping, and accounting processes.

- *Production activities*, which are the physical tasks employees must perform to produce a product or deliver a service.

- *Material flow*, the physical movement of materials from receiving, through production, to the shipment or delivery of finished goods or services.

- *Customer value*, which is an aspect of a product or service for which a customer is willing to pay. (This is sometimes referred to as "value added.")

- A *push system*, where materials are automatically moved from one operation to the next, whether or not they are needed.

- A *pull system*, where materials are moved from one operation to the next based on a request from the next operation.

- Any waste involved in your business or manufacturing processes.

- *Takt time*, which is the total available work time per day (or shift) divided by customer-demand requirements per day (or shift). Takt time sets the pace of production to match the rate of customer demand.

- *Lead time*, which is the time it takes to complete an activity from start to finish.

- You also need to become familiar with four types of icons, described in detail later in this chapter:

  1. Production-flow icons

  2. Material-flow icons

  3. Information-flow icons

  4. Lean manufacturing icons

Tip If you work in a manufacturing organization, at the beginning of your lean manufacturing initiative you should make a value stream map at the plant level only. As your initiative progresses, you might decide to depict an entire system for multiple plants or for your entire company.

How do I create a value stream map?

To begin, all employees should map the value stream by themselves. Usually, each employee's map will be different from all the others. Then, by comparing maps and working together to reach a consensus, your work team can develop the most accurate map of the value stream possible.

1. Assemble paper, pencils, erasers, and a stopwatch for collecting data.

2. Select a product or service to map. Conduct a quick tour of the value stream to view the end-to-end material and information flows, making sure that you have identified all the component flows.

    Tip Don't work from memory. Observe the value stream in action. Interview each team member on every shift, if applicable. Verify your observations against documented procedures, routings, job aids, and memoranda.

    Tip Remember to record exactly what you see without making any judgments. Don't waste time debating the merits of an activity or its proper sequence; just record what is happening.

3. Identify a representative customer of the product or service under review. Once you have identified a typical customer, gather data about typical order quantities, delivery frequencies, and number of product or service variations. This information will

help you establish the takt time for the customer and the product.

4. Begin mapping the value stream, starting with customer requirements and going through the major production activities. The result is a current-state map of the value stream.

   Tip Begin mapping the value stream by drawing on Post-it® Notes, which can be easily rearranged while your team comes to a consensus, or use a pencil and eraser to draw and refine your map.

5. Add production-flow, material-flow, information-flow, and lean manufacturing icons (see pages 20–23 for details) to your value stream map.

   Tip During data collection, show whether information is communicated in real time or in batches. If it is communicated in batches, show the size of the batches, how often they are sent, and the *process delay* (see Glossary).

   Tip Identify every location where material is stored, sits idle, or is moved.

   Tip If your company uses a kanban production-control system (see chapter 9, "The Kanban System," for details), show the use of load-leveling boxes or individual kanban posts (mailboxes). Also show where the physical kanbans are used.

   Tip Identify all non-value-added activities in all the production, material, and information flows.

6. Create a lead-time chart at the bottom of your value stream map, showing the value-added and non-value-added production lead times.

7. Review the map with all the employees who work in the value stream you have mapped to ensure you haven't missed any activities or materials.

Sample Production-Flow Icons

1. **Department or manufacturing process**. The top of the icon shows the name of the department or the process being mapped. The bottom of the icon shows resources, information, or a relevant lean-enterprise technique.

Machining
Automated
Production Scheduling

2. **Outside sources**. These include customers and suppliers. Try to use typical customers or suppliers for your mapping activities.

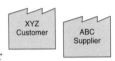

XYZ Customer   ABC Supplier

3. **Data box**. This is a place for key data such as machine availability; number of product variations

C/T = 45 sec.	KPC = taste
C/O = 30 min.	KCC = temp.
3 shifts	Process stds.
2% scrap	Product specs

that each operation typically produces; product changeover times; whether each part you produce can be run daily, weekly, or monthly; cycle time; process capacity; and first-time-through (FTT) quality levels (see Glossary). If the process you are mapping is machine based, record its overall equipment efficiency, or OEE, rate (see Glossary) and then identify which operation is the constraining operation.

4. **People**. Shows the number of employees required to perform an operation. "Partial people" can be used; for example, "0.5" means that an employee spends half of his/her time performing a particular operation.

1

Sample Material-Flow Icons

1. **Push movement of production materials.** Shows the movement of raw materials or components that are "pushed" by the production process rather than being requested by the customer.

2. **Pull movement of production materials.** Shows the movement of raw materials or components that are requested by the customer (i.e., they are not pushed).

3. **Automated movement of production materials.** Indicates that automation is used to move raw materials or components from one process to another.

4. **FIFO.** Indicates that products need to be pulled and delivered on a first-in, first-out (FIFO) basis: the oldest remaining items in a batch are the first to move forward in the production process.

5. **Rail shipment.** Shows the movement of materials by train. Be sure to show the frequency of shipments on your map.

6. **Truck shipment.** Shows the movement of materials by truck. Be sure to show the frequency of shipments on your map.

7. **Air shipment.** Shows the movement of materials by plane. Be sure to show the frequency of shipments on your map.

8. **Inventory.** Indicates the inventory count and time.

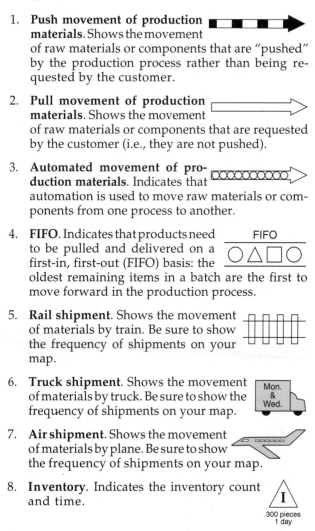

9. **Storage**. Shows all products contained in a storage area. You can note the minimum and maximum levels within each bin or row location.

10. **Emergency stock**. Shows all products contained in an emergency-stock area. You can note the minimum and maximum levels of each item.

A
B
C

Sample Information-Flow Icons

1. **Manual information flow.** Shows information that is transferred by hand.

2. **Electronic information flow.** Shows information that is transferred via computer.

3. **Information type.** Indicates the type of information being communicated.

    Weekly Schedule

4. **Production kanban**. A card used to initiate the production of a certain item. (Used for kanban systems only; see chapter 9, "The Kanban System," for details.)

    20

5. **Withdrawal kanban**. A card used to obtain an item from a storage area. (Used for kanban systems only.)

6. **Signal kanban**. A card used to initiate a batch operation. (Used for kanban systems only.)

7. **Kanban card post**. This indicates the use of a physical mailbox location for kanbans. It is used for kanban systems only. (See chapter 9 for details.)

8. **Load leveling box**. Used for kanban systems to indicate load leveling (see Glossary). (See chapter 9 for details.)

 ©2002 GOAL/QPC

Sample Lean Manufacturing Icons

1. **Visual management**. Shows that visual management techniques (see chapter 4, "Visual Management," for details) have been applied.

2. **Error proofing**. Shows that error-proofing techniques (see chapter 5, "Error-Proofing," for details) have been applied.

3. **Quick changeover**. Indicates that quick changeover techniques (see chapter 6, "Quick Changeover," for details) have been applied.

4. **Product and process standards**. Shows that your company's product and process standards are in place.

5. **Stretch objectives**. Shows where stretch objectives for fostering improvement have been set for specific operations or for the value stream as a whole.

6. **Performance boards**. Indicates that process objectives and results have been posted in an operation's work area.

7. **Constraining operation**. Shows which operation(s) constrains, or limits, the progress of the value stream.

A Sample Value Stream

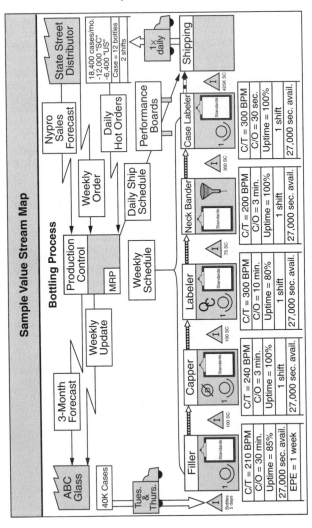

How do I use my team's value stream map to make future improvements in my organization?

After your team completes a map showing your organization's value stream in its current state, what's next? First, familiarize yourself with the lean methods and tools outlined in this book. Then consider the ideas below as you review your value stream map to plan future improvements for your organization.

Look at your takt time

- Your goal is to get your organization's value stream to produce to the takt time. You can calculate the takt time that your production or business processes must meet by using the following formula:

$$\text{takt time} = \frac{\text{available daily production time}}{\begin{array}{c}\text{required daily quantity of output}\\ \text{(i.e., customer demand)}\end{array}}$$

When the value stream produces ahead of the takt time, overproduction occurs; when it produces behind the takt time, under-production occurs. If your value stream is not producing to the takt time, investigate possible causes. What processes might be negatively affecting production?

- Are you producing finished goods only to add them to inventory, or are your sales and operations activities integrated so that your production schedules are based on actual customer orders? Remember, your goal is to have your value stream driven by customer orders. It is also beneficial to minimize inventory in the production channel. This frees up your capacity, and you will then be able to meet smaller-order quantities more frequently.

Apply one-piece-flow principles

Does your value stream have large batch and process delays (see Glossary) that add to your lead time? Such delays can occur in your production, material, or information flows. To eliminate batch and process delays, try applying one-piece-flow principles to your value stream. (See chapter 8, "One-Piece Flow," for details.)

Apply quick-changeover, error-proofing, and visual management techniques

- Can you use quick-changeover methods to reduce your setup costs and batch sizes? (See chapter 6, "Quick Changeover," for details.) By reducing changeover times, your company will be able to run smaller batch sizes and free up production capacity. If being able to offer a mix of products and services is important, then quick changeover will reduce the number of operations you need to run every day, week, or month.

- Can you use error-proofing techniques to ensure that no product defects are being passed on to downstream operations? (See chapter 5, "Error Proofing," for details.) As batch sizes get smaller, the impact of product defects on your production schedules gets bigger. This is especially true if defects shut down operations.

- Have you conducted visual management activities, such as the 5 S's, in your important operational areas? (See chapter 4, "Visual Management," for details.) A well-organized and well-maintained workplace is key to ensuring that all employees perform their duties correctly and in a safe and proper manner, which ensures quality results.

Apply work-standardization techniques

Are your work standards displayed at each workstation? Are they easy to understand? Do they reflect current practices? Proper work instructions ensure that the correct decisions and physical tasks are being performed to meet lead-time, waste-reduction, and cost objectives.

Use load leveling

• Once you have applied one-piece-flow, quick-changeover, error-proofing, visual management, and work-standardization techniques, try using load leveling in your value stream. This prevents overproduction and under-production.

For example, if one of your customers needs ten blues, twenty greens, and thirty yellows per five-day workweek, your objective is to build two blues, four greens, and six yellows each day. Then, if the customer decides to decrease or increase the order during the week, you can immediately respond by changing your production schedules to keep producing to the takt time.

• Check your build sequence. This can have a significant impact on your changeover times and product availability. Does your build sequence work well with your planned production volumes and mix? For example, it may be better to build two blues, then six yellows, and then four greens, rather than building four greens first. Eventually, you should develop a plan for every part of your build sequence that takes into account customer-service levels and production mix and volumes.

Establish lean metrics

Establish metrics for your value stream to make sure that you are meeting lead-time, waste-reduction, and cost objectives. Refer to chapter 11, "Lean Metrics," for an introduction to core-process measures that you can apply to your organization's value stream.

Use other tools to complement your value stream map

You can obtain excellent insight into your organization's current and future operational practices by using a value stream map in conjunction with flowcharts (see *The Problem Solving Memory Jogger*™ for details) and a workflow diagram (see chapter 7, "Standard Operations," for details).

Because the value stream map provides you with a "big picture" view of several interconnected activities, it is a good place to start. You can then further describe the details of specific work processes using flow-charting techniques.

A workflow diagram is useful for gathering physical information, such as the distance between work operations and the movement of employees and materials. It is possible to record such information on a value stream map, but it is more easily viewed and understood when you include it on a workflow diagram.

Chapter 4
Visual Management

What is it?

Visual management is a set of techniques that 1) expose waste so you can eliminate it and prevent it from recurring in the future, 2) make your company's operation standards known to all employees so they can easily follow them, and 3) improve workplace efficiency through organization. Implementing these techniques involves three steps:

- Organizing your workplace by using a method known as the 5 S's (sort, shine, set in order, standardize, and sustain); see page 32 for details.

- Ensuring that all your required work standards and related information are displayed in the workplace.

- Controlling all your workplace processes by exposing and stopping errors—and preventing them in the future.

What does it do?

Using visual management techniques enables your company to do the following:

1. Improve the "first-time-through" quality of your products or services by creating an environment that:

- Prevents most errors and defects before they occur.

- Detects the errors and defects that do occur and enables rapid response and correction.

- Establishes and maintains standards for zero errors, defects, and waste.

2. Improve workplace safety and employee health by:

   - Removing hazards.

   - Improving communication by sharing information openly throughout the company.

   - Creating compliance with all work standards, reporting deviations, and responding quickly to problems.

3. Improve the overall efficiency of your workplace and equipment, enabling your organization to meet customer expectations.

4. Lower your total costs.

Why use it?

Creating an organized, efficient, cleaner workplace that has clear work processes and standards helps your company lower its costs. Also, employees' job satisfaction improves when their work environment makes it easier for them to get the job done right.

What areas should I focus on?

You can effectively gain control over your company's manufacturing or business processes by focusing on the following areas:

- Value-added activities. These are activities that change the form or function of your product or service.

- Information sharing. This is the distribution of the right information to the right people at the right time, in the most useful form possible.

- Source inspections. The goal of these inspections is to discover the source of errors that cause defects in either your products or business processes.

- Material quantities and flow. All work operations should result in the correct quantities of materials or process steps moving as required for downstream operations.

- Health and safety. All work processes, facilities, and equipment design and procedures should contribute to the maintenance of a safe and healthy workplace.

It is most effective to focus on the areas listed above as they relate to six aspects of your production or business processes:

1. The quality of incoming, in-process, and outgoing materials.

2. Work processes and methods of operation.

3. Equipment, machines, and tools.

4. Storage, inventory, and supplies.

5. Safety and safety training.

6. Information sharing.

> **Tip** To gain control over your processes, you must understand the "three actuals":
> - The actual place or location in which a process occurs.
> - The actual employees working in that location.
> - The actual process occurring in that location.

Mapping the process will help you understand all three actuals. (For details about mapping, see the "Set in order" section on page 34.)

Getting started

Before you begin to implement visual management techniques, make sure you do the following:

- Elect an employee from each work team to lead the program and remove any barriers his or her team encounters along the way.

- Train all involved employees about the visual management techniques outlined below.

- Tell everyone in the areas of your plant or office that will be involved about the program. Also give a "heads up" to other employees or departments that might be affected by it.

- Create storage ("red tag") areas for holding materials you will remove from work sites in your plant or building.

- Create a location for supplies you will need as you progress through your visual management program, such as tags, cleaning materials, paint, labels, marking tape, and sign materials.

- Coordinate the program with your maintenance department and any other departments that you might need to call on for help.

- Make sure that all employees understand and follow your company's safety regulations and procedures as they make changes.

How to do it

The 5 S's

1. **Sort.** Sort through the items in your work area, following the steps below. Your goal is to keep what is needed and remove everything else.

   a. Reduce the number of items in your immediate work area to just what you actually need.

©2002 GOAL/QPC

b. Find appropriate locations for all these items, keeping in mind their size and weight, how frequently you use them, and how urgently you might need them.

c. Find another storage area for all supplies that you need but do not use every day.

d. Decide how you will prevent the accumulation of unnecessary items in the future.

e. Tape or tie red tags to all the items you remove from your work area. Place the items in a temporary "red-tag storage" area for five days. Either use the Sorting Criteria chart on page 38 as a guide for disposing of items or develop your own criteria.

f. After five days, move any item that you haven't needed to a central red-tag storage area for another thirty days. You can then sort through all items stored there to see if they might be of any use and throw away everything else, remembering to follow your company policy. Use a logbook to track what you do with all red-tag items.

Tip If employees disagree about what to do with some of the materials, try to resolve the conflict through discussion. They can also consult their managers about the materials' value, current and potential use, and impact on workplace performance.

2. **Shine**. Clean and "shine" your workplace by eliminating all forms of contamination, including dirt, dust, fluids, and other debris. Cleaning is also a good time to inspect your equipment to look for abnormal wear or conditions that might lead to equipment failure.

Once your cleaning process is complete, find ways to eliminate all sources of contamination and to keep your workplace clean at all times.

Tip Keeping equipment clean and "shiny" should be a part of your maintenance process. Your company's equipment maintenance training should teach the concepts of "cleaning as inspection" and "eliminating sources of contamination."

Tip Remember that your workplace includes not just the plant floor, but your administrative, sales, purchasing, accounting, and engineering areas as well. You can clean these areas by archiving project drawings when they are completed and properly storing vendor catalogs and product information. Decide what methods (local or shared hard drives, floppy disks, or CDs) are the best for storing your electronic files.

3. **Set in order**. During this step, you evaluate and improve the efficiency of your current *workflow*, the steps and motions employees take to perform their work tasks. (See chapter 3, "Mapping the Value Stream.")

   a. Create a map of your workspace that shows where all the equipment and tools are currently located. Draw lines to show the steps that employees must take to perform their work tasks.

   b. Use the map to identify wasted motion or <u>congestion</u> caused by <u>excessive</u> distances traveled, unnecessary movement, and improper placement of tools and materials.

   c. Draw a map of a more efficient workspace, showing the rearrangement of every item that needs to be moved.

   d. On your map, create *location indicators* for each item. These are markers that show where and how much material should be kept in a specific place. Once you create your new workspace, you can hang up location indicators within it.

---

e. Make a plan for relocating items that need to be moved so you can make your new, efficient workspace a reality. (See the "Set in Order Work Sheet" below.) As you do this step, ask yourself the following questions:

- Who will approve the plan?
- Who will move the items?
- Are there any rules, policies, or regulations that affect the location of these items? Will employees be able to adhere to these rules?
- When is the best time to relocate these items?
- Do we need any special equipment to move the items?

Tip As a team, brainstorm your ideas for new ways to lay out your workspace. If it is impractical or impossible to move an item the way you would like, redesign the rest of the workspace around this item's location.

f. Post the drawing of the new workplace layout in your area.

Set in Order Work Sheet						
Item to Relocate	Old Location	Proposed Location	Apprvd. by	Given to	Relocation Timing	Status
Date: Dept.: Prepared by:						

4. **Standardize**. Make sure that team members from every work area follow the sort, shine, and set-in-order steps. Share information among teams so that there is no confusion or errors regarding:

a. Locations

b. Delivery

c. Destinations

d. Quantities

e. Schedules

f. Downtime

g. Procedures and standards

As you begin to use your newly organized workplace, have everyone write down their ideas for reducing clutter, eliminating unnecessary items, organizing, making cleaning easier, establishing standard procedures, and making it easier for employees to follow the rules.

Once you have standardized your methods, make your standards known to everyone so that anything out of place or not in compliance with your procedure will be immediately noticed.

5. **Sustain**. The gains you make during the above four steps are sustained when:

a. All employees are properly trained.

b All employees use visual management techniques.

c. All managers are committed to the program's success.

d. The workplace is well ordered and adheres to the new procedures all your employees have agreed upon.

e. Your new procedures become a habit for all employees.

Reevaluate your workspace using the Sustain Evaluation Form (see the figure below) as needed. Encourage and recognize the achievement of all work areas that are able to sustain their visual management efforts. This helps your company to maintain a cycle of continuous improvement.

Sustain Evaluation Form			
Visual Management "Sustain" Evaluation		Yes/ No	Comments
Sort	• Are all items in the work area necessary? • Have unnecessary items been red-tagged? • Have red-tagged items been removed?	Yes	All moved to red-tag area
Shine	• Have all areas been cleaned? • Has a cleaning schedule been established?	Yes	Schedule set; training under way
Set in Order	• Is the location for every item in the work area defined? • Is every item in its defined location?		
Standardize	• Have standards been established? • Are standards posted? • Have company-wide standards been adopted in the area?		
Sustain	• Is the evaluation being completed on a regular basis? • Are all schedules, such as the cleaning schedule, being followed?		

Sorting Criteria

Frequency of Use	Action
Never (unneeded)	Throw away
Once a year	Place in storage
Less than once a month	Store in factory or office
Once a week	Store in general work area
Once a day or more	Carry or keep at workstation

Questions to Ask:

What is this item used for?
How often is it needed?
Is it needed in this location? Anywhere else?
How many are needed?
Who uses it?
How easy is it to replace?
What might happen if it were not available when it was needed?
How much space does it occupy?
Are there any other reasons why this item should be kept here?

Red Tag Information

Red tags typically contain the following information. You can adapt this list to best suit your company's needs.

Item
Name
Quantity
Identification (inventory control number)
Approximate value
Date item tagged and reason
Department, shift, operator
Disposal method
Red-tag holding area log-in date
Holding area removal disposal date
Authorized by: _____

deviation [divi'eʃən] n.
偏差

*standard deviation
標準差

Chapter 5
Error Proofing
防錯

What is it?

Error proofing is a structured approach to ensuring quality all the way through your work processes. This approach enables you to improve your production or business processes to prevent specific errors—and, thus, defects—from occurring.

What does it do?

Error-proofing methods enable you to discover sources of errors through fact-based problem solving. The focus of error proofing is not on identifying and counting defects. Rather, it is on the elimination of their cause: one or more errors that occur somewhere in the production process. The distinction [dɪ'stɪŋkʃən] n. 差別 between an error and a defect is as follows:

- An *error* is any deviation from a specified manufacturing or business process. Errors cause defects in products or services.

- A *defect* is a part, product, or service that does not conform to specifications or a customer's expectations. Defects are caused by errors.

The goal of error proofing is to create an error-free production environment. It prevents defects by eliminating their root cause, which is the best way to produce high-quality products and services.

strive v.
[straɪv] 努力

exceed [ɪk'siːd] 超过

Why use it?

For your organization to be competitive in the marketplace, you must deliver high-quality products and services that _exceed_ your customers' expectations. You cannot afford to produce defective products or services.

A lean enterprise _strives_ for quality at the source. This means that any defects that occur during one operation in a manufacturing or business process should never be passed on to the next operation. This ensures that your customers will receive only defect-free products or services.

In a "fat" system, any defects that are found can simply be _discarded_ while operations continue. These defects are later counted, and if their numbers are high enough, root-cause analysis (see Glossary) is done to prevent their _recurrence_. But in a lean enterprise, which concentrates on producing smaller batch sizes and producing to order versus adding to inventory, a single defect can significantly impact performance levels.

When a defect occurs in a lean enterprise, operations must stop while immediate action is taken to resolve the situation. Obviously, such pauses in operations can be costly if defects occur often. Therefore, it is important to prevent defects before they can occur.

What areas do I focus on? LEADER

Your organization can achieve zero errors by understanding and implementing the four elements of error proofing. These are as follows:

versus [ˈvɜːsəs] 对抗

1. General inspection.

2. 100% inspection.

3. Error-proofing devices.

4. Immediate feedback.

---

detect [dɪ'tɛkt] v. 察覺
occurrence [ə'kɜːrəns] n. 發生

Below is an in-depth look at each of these four elements.

Element #1: General inspection

The first, and most important, element of error proofing is inspection. There are three types of inspections that organizations commonly use.

drawback
n. 缺點

1. Source inspections. Source inspections detect errors in a manufacturing process before a defect in the final part or product occurs. The goal of source inspections is to prevent the occurrence of defects by preventing the occurrence of errors.

   In addition to catching errors, source inspections provide feedback to employees before further processing takes place. Source inspections are often the most challenging element of error proofing to design and implement.

2. Judgment inspections. Often referred to as end-of-the-line inspections, final inspections, or dock audits, these are inspections during which a quality inspector or operator compares a final product or part with a standard. If the product or part does not conform, it is rejected.

   This inspection method has two drawbacks. First, it might not prevent all defects from being shipped to customers. Second, it increases the delay between the time an error occurs and the time a resulting defect is discovered. This allows the production process to continue to make defective products and makes root-cause analysis difficult.

   Tip If you rely on judgment inspections, it's important to relay inspection results to all the earlier steps in your production process. This way, information about a defect is communicated to the point in the process at which the problem originated.

3. Informative inspections. Informative inspections provide timely information about a defect so that root-cause analysis can be done and the production process can be adjusted before significant numbers of defects are created.

Typically, these inspections are done close enough to the time of the occurrence of the defect so that action can be taken to prevent further defects from occurring.

There are two types of informative inspections. They are as follows:

- **Successive inspections**. These inspections are performed after one operation in the production process is completed, by employees who perform the next operation in the process. Feedback can be provided as soon as any defects are detected (which is preferable) or simply tracked and reported later. It is always better to report defects immediately.

- **Self-inspections**. Operators perform self-inspections at their own workstations. If an operator finds a defect in a product or part, he/she sets it aside and takes action to ensure that other defective products or parts are not passed on to the next operation. The root cause of the defect is then determined and corrected. Often this involves putting error-proofing measures and devices in place to prevent the problem from recurring.

Tip Industrial engineering studies have shown that human visual inspection is only about 85% effective. Similar inaccuracies happen when humans directly measure physical properties, such as pressure, temperature, time, and distance. Use electronic or mechanical inspection devices to achieve better accuracy.

Tip Operator self-inspection is the second most effective type of inspection. It is much more effective and timely than successive inspection. The number of errors detected depends on the diligence of the operator and the difficulty of detecting the defect.

Tip Wherever practical, empower operators to stop the production line whenever a defect is detected. This creates a sense of urgency that focuses employees' energy on prevention of the defect's recurrence. It also creates the need for effective source inspections and self-inspections.

Element #2: 100% inspection

The second element of error proofing is 100% inspection, the most effective type of inspection. During these inspections, a comparison of actual parts or products to standards is done 100% of the time at the potential source of an error. The goal is to achieve 100% real-time inspection of the potential process errors that lead to defects.

It is often physically impossible and too time-consuming to conduct 100% inspection of all products or parts for defects. To help you achieve zero defects, use low-cost error-proofing devices (see page 44) to perform 100% inspection of known sources of error. When an error is found, you should halt the process or alert an operator before a defect can be produced.

Tip Zero defects is an achievable goal! Many organizations have attained this level of error proofing. One of the largest barriers to achieving it is the belief that it can't be done. By changing this belief among your employees, you can make zero defects a reality in your organization.

Statistical process control (SPC) is the use of mathematics and statistical measurements to solve your organization's problems and build quality into your products and services. When used to monitor product characteristics, SPC is an effective technique for diagnosing process-performance problems and gathering information for improving your production process.

But because SPC relies on product sampling to provide both product and process characteristics, it can detect only those errors that occur in the sample that you analyze. It gives a reliable estimate of the number of total defects that are occurring, but it cannot prevent defects from happening, nor does it identify all the defective products that exist before they reach your customers.

Element #3: Error-proofing devices

The third element of error proofing is the use of error-proofing devices: physical devices that enhance or substitute for the human senses and improve both the cost and reliability of your organization's inspection activities.

You can use mechanical, electrical, pneumatic, or hydraulic devices to sense, signal, or prevent existing or potential error conditions and thus achieve 100% inspection of errors in a cost-effective manner.

Common error-proofing devices include the following:

- Guide pins of different sizes that physically capture or limit the movement of parts, tooling, or equipment during the production process.

- Limit switches, physical-contact sensors that show the presence and/or absence of products and machine components and their proper position.

- Counters, devices used to count the number of components, production of parts, and availability of components.

- Alarms that an operator activates when he/she detects an error.

- Checklists, which are written or graphical reminders of tasks, materials, events, and so on.

Such industrial sensing devices are the most versatile error-proofing tools available for work processes. Once such a device detects an unacceptable condition, it either warns the operator of the condition or automatically takes control of the function of the equipment, causing it to stop or correct itself. These warning and control steps, known as *regulatory functions*, are explained more below.

These sensing devices can detect object characteristics by using both contact and non-contact methods. Contact sensors include micro-switches and limit switches; non-contact methods include transmitting and reflecting photoelectric switches.

Setting functions describe specific attributes that sensing devices need to inspect. All of the four setting functions listed below are effective error-detection methods:

1. Contact methods involve inspecting for physical characteristics of an object, such as size, shape, or color, to determine if any abnormalities exist.

   Example: A sensor receives a reflective signal (sparks) only when the flintwheel is installed correctly.

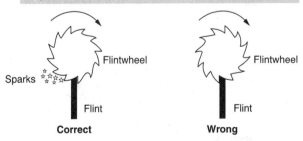

Figure courtesy of Allen Bradley

2. Fixed-value setting functions inspect for a specific number of items, events, and so on, to determine if any abnormalities exist. This technique is often used to ensure that the right quantity of parts has been used or the correct number of activities has been performed.

Example: All materials must be used to assemble a case, including eight screws. A counter on the drill keeps track of the number of screws used. Another method is to package screws in groups of eight.

3. Motion-step setting functions inspect the sequence of actions to determine if they are done out of order.

Example: Materials are loaded into a hopper in a predetermined sequence. If the scale does not indicate the correct weight for each incremental addition, a warning light comes on.

4. Information-setting functions check the accuracy of information and its movement over time and distance to determine if any gaps or errors exist.

Here are some tips for using information-setting functions:

- To capture information that will be needed later, use work logs, schedules, and action lists.

- To distribute information accurately across distances, you can use e-mail, bar-coding systems, radio frequency devices, voice messaging systems, and integrated information systems, such as enterprise resource planning (ERP) (see Glossary).

Example: Inventory placed in a temporary storage location must be accurately entered into the storeroom system for later retrieval during the picking operation. Bar-coding is used to identify part numbers and bin locations. This data is transferred directly from the bar-code reader to the storeroom system. Customers access the storeroom system through the internet.

Element #4: Immediate feedback

The fourth element of error proofing is immediate feedback. Because time is of the essence in lean operations, giving immediate feedback to employees who can resolve errors before defects occur is vital to success.

The ideal response to an error is to stop production and eliminate the source of the error. But this is not always possible, especially in continuous batch or flow operations. (See chapter 8 for details.) You should determine the most cost-effective scenario for stopping production in your work process when an error is detected.

It is often better to use a sensor or other error-proofing device to improve feedback time rather than relying on human intervention.

Methods for providing immediate feedback that use sensing devices are called *regulatory functions*. When a sensing device detects an error, it either warns an operator of the condition or makes adjustments to correct the error.

There are two types of regulatory functions. The first, the *warning method*, does not stop operations but provides various forms of feedback for the operator to act upon. Common feedback methods include flashing lights or unusual sounds designed to capture an operator's attention.

Example: A clogged meter sets off a warning light on a control panel. However, the operator can still run the mixer and produce bad powder.

The second type of regulatory function is called the *control method*. This method is preferred for responding to error conditions, especially where safety is a concern. However, it can also be a more frustrating method for the operator if a machine continually shuts itself down.

Example: A mixer will not operate until the water meter is repaired. The preventive maintenance program should have "meter visual inspections" on its schedule, and spare nozzles should be made available.

Warning methods are less effective than control methods because they rely on the operator's ability to recognize and correct the situation. If the operator does not notice or react to the error quickly enough, defective parts or products will still be produced. However, warning methods are preferred over control methods when the automatic shutdown of a line or piece of equipment is very expensive.

> **Tip** Don't let an error-proofing device sit idle! This happens all too often when people override sensors, disconnect them, or ignore them. If your employees are tempted to disconnect an error-proofing device, then install an error-proofing device for the error-proofing device.

What are some common sources of errors?

Common sources of error include humans, methods, measurements, materials, machines, and environmental conditions. These are examined in detail below.

Any one of these factors alone, or any combination of them, might be enough to cause errors, which can then lead to defects.

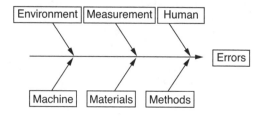

©2002 GOAL/QPC

1. **Humans**. Unfortunately, human error is an unavoidable reality. The reasons are many. See the chart below for a list of reasons.

Reasons for Human Error
Lack of knowledge, skills, or ability. This happens when employees have not received proper training to perform a task and their skill or knowledge level is not verified.
Mental errors. These include slips and mistakes. *Slips* are subconscious actions. They usually occur when an experienced employee forgets to perform a task. *Mistakes* are conscious actions. They occur when an employee decides to perform a task in a way that results in an error.
Sensory overload. A person's ability to perceive, recognize, and respond to stimuli is dramatically affected by the sharpness of the five senses. When an employee's senses are bombarded by too many stimuli at once, sensory overload results, and his/her senses are dulled. This increases the chance for error.
Mechanical process errors. Some tasks are physically difficult to do and are thus prone to error. They can result in repetitive-strain injuries and physical exhaustion, which are both known to cause errors.
Distractions. There are two types of distractions: internal and external. External distractions include high-traffic areas, loud conversations, and ringing phones. Emotional stress and daydreaming are examples of internal distractions. Both types can lead to errors.
Loss of memory. Many work tasks require employees to recall information that can be forgotten. In addition, aging, drug or alcohol use, and fatigue can all cause memory loss and lead to errors.
Loss of emotional control. Anger, sorrow, jealousy, and fear often work as emotional blinders, hampering employees' ability to work effectively.

2. **Measurements**. Measurements must be accurate, repeatable, and reproducible if they are to successfully locate a problem. Unfortunately, measurement

devices and methods are as equally prone to error as the processes and products that they measure.

Inspection measurement practices, measurement graphs and reports, and measurement definitions are all potential sources of misinterpretation and disagreement. For instance, a measurement scale's being out of calibration can cause errors.

Tip Don't be surprised if a root-cause analysis points to measurement as the source of an error. An accurate measurement is the product of many factors, including humans, machines, and methods.

3. **Methods**. Industry experts believe that nearly 85% of the errors that occur in a work process are caused by the tasks and technology involved in the process. The sources of error in a work process are as follows:

- **Process steps**. These are the physical or mental steps that convert raw materials into products, parts, or services.

- **Transportation**. This refers to the movement of materials, information, people, and technology during a work process.

- **Decision making**. This is the process of making a choice among alternatives. Make sure that all your employees' decisions address six basic questions: Who? What? When? Where? How? Why?

- **Inspections**. These are activities that compare the actual to the expected. As noted above, they are prone to error.

Tip The area of work processes is the one where lean enterprises make the largest gains in error reduction and quality improvement. Concentrate your organizational efforts on this area.

---

4. **Materials**. This factor can contribute to error in the following ways:

   - Use of the wrong type or amount of raw materials or use of incompatible raw materials, components, or finished products.

   - Inherent product, tool, or equipment designs. A root-cause analysis typically leads back to faulty manufacturing, materials handling, or packaging practices.

   - Missing or ill-designed administrative tools (e.g., forms, documents, and office supplies) that do not support performance requirements.

5. **Machines**. Machine errors are classified as either predictable or unpredictable. Predictable errors are usually addressed in a preventative or scheduled maintenance plan (see Glossary). Unpredictable errors, which are caused by varying machine reliability, should be considered when your organization purchases equipment. If satisfactory machine reliability cannot be achieved, then you must plan other ways to prevent and catch machine-related errors.

6. **Environmental conditions**. Poor lighting, excessive heat or cold, and high noise levels all have a dramatic affect on human attention levels, energy levels, and reasoning ability.

In addition, unseen organizational influences—such as pressure to get a product shipped, internal competition among employees, and pressure to achieve higher wage levels—all affect quality and productivity..

> **Tip** Error-proofing devices and techniques can be used for some, but not all, sources of environmentally caused errors. Often an organization's operating and personnel policies must be revised to achieve a goal of zero defects.

How do I error-proof "red-flag" conditions?

The probability that errors will happen is high in certain types of situations. These so-called red-flag conditions include the following:

Red-Flag Conditions

Lack of an effective standard. *Standard operating procedures (SOPs)* are reliable instructions that describe the correct and most effective way to get a work process done. Without SOPs, employees cannot know the quality of the product or service they produce or know with certainty when an error has occurred. In addition, when there are no SOPs, or if the SOPs are complicated or hard to understand, variations can occur in the way a task is completed, resulting in errors.

Symmetry. This is when opposite sides of a part, tool, material, or fixture are, or seem to be, identical. The identical sides of a symmetrical object can be confused during an operation, resulting in errors.

Asymmetry. This is when opposite sides of a part, tool, material, or fixture are different in size, shape, or relative position. Slight differences are difficult to notice in asymmetrical parts, leading to confusion, delays, or errors.

Rapid repetition. This is when the same action or operation is performed quickly, over and over again. Rapidly repeating a task, whether manually or by machine, increases the opportunity for error.

High or extremely high volume. This refers to rapidly repeated tasks that have a very large output. Pressure to produce high volumes makes it difficult for an employee to follow the SOPs, increasing the opportunity for errors.

Poor environmental conditions. Dim lighting, poor ventilation, inadequate housekeeping, and too much traffic density or poorly directed traffic can cause errors. The presence of foreign materials (e.g., dirt or oils), over-handling, and excessive transportation can also result in errors or damaged products and parts.

Continued on the next page

Red-Flag Conditions (continued)

Adjustments. These include bringing parts, tooling, or fixtures into a correct relative position.

Tooling and tooling changes. These occur when any working part of a power-driven machine needs to be changed, either because of wear or breakage or to allow production of different parts or to different specifications.

Dimensions, specifications, and critical conditions. Dimensions are measurements used to determine the precise position or location for a part or product, including height, width, length, and depth. Specifications and critical conditions include temperature, pressure, speed, tension coordinates, number, and volume. Deviation from exact dimensions or variation from standards leads to errors.

Many or mixed parts. Some work processes involve a wide range of parts in varying quantities and mixes. Selecting the right part and the right quantity becomes more difficult when there are many of them or when they look similar.

Multiple steps. Most work processes involve many small operations or sub-steps that must be done, often in a preset, strict order. If an employee forgets a step, does the steps in an incorrect sequence, or mistakenly repeats a step, errors occur and defects result.

Infrequent production. This refers to an operation or task that is not done on a regular basis. Irregular or infrequent performance of a task leads to the increased likelihood that employees will forget the proper procedures or specifications for the task. The risk of error increases even more when these operations are complicated.

Tip Always use data as a basis for making adjustments in your work processes. Using subjective opinion or intuition to make adjustments can result in errors—and eventually defects.

Tip Any change in conditions can lead to errors that in turn lead to defects. For instance, wear or degradation of production equipment produces slow changes that occur without the operator's awareness and can lead to the production of defective parts.

How do I error-proof my production process?

An effective way of error-proofing your work processes is to use the 7-Step Problem-Solving Model, a systematic model for solving problems. You use this model to identify errors, create solutions, and prevent the errors from happening again.

During this process, inspections are performed and error-proofing devices are installed during Step 4, which involves developing a solution and action plan.

Since all production processes are affected by product and machine design, work methods, employees' skill levels, and supporting technology, you must consider these factors during your error-proofing activities. A snapshot of the 7-Step Model is shown below.

The 7-Step Problem-Solving Model

1. Describe the problem

2. Describe the current process

3. Identify the root cause(s)

4. Develop a solution and action plan

5. Implement the solution

6. Review and evaluate the results

7. Reflect and act on learnings

(Note: An in-depth discussion of the 7-Step Problem-Solving Model is beyond the scope of this book. For a complete description, please refer to *The Problem-Solving Memory Jogger*™.)

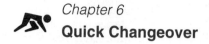

Chapter 6
Quick Changeover

What is it?

Quick changeover is a method of analyzing your organization's manufacturing processes and then reducing the materials, skilled resources, and time required for equipment setup, including the exchange of tools and dies.

What does it do?

Using the quick-changeover method helps your production teams reduce downtime by improving the setup process for new product launches and product changeovers, as well as improving associated maintenance activities. In addition, it allows your organization to cost-effectively implement small-batch production or one-piece flow. (See chapter 8, "One-Piece Flow," for details.)

Why use it?

There are many advantages to using the quick-changeover method. These include the following:

- Members of your team can respond to changes in product demand more quickly.

- Machine capacity is increased, which allows for greater production capacity.

- Manufacturing errors are reduced.

- Changeovers are made more safely.

- You can reduce your inventory (and its associated costs) because it is no longer needed for extended downtimes.

- Once you can make changeovers according to an established procedure, you can train additional operators to perform these tasks, which increases the flexibility of your organization.

- Lead times are shortened, improving your organization's competitive position in the marketplace.

What skills and concepts do I need to know?

Before you get started with the quick-changeover process, all members of your work team should become familiar with the following key skills and concepts:

- The difference between internal and external processes. *Internal processes* are activities that an equipment operator must perform while the production line is idle. *External processes* are activities that can be performed while the line is still running.

- How to create a matrix diagram and a check sheet. (See *The Memory Jogger*™ *II* for details.)

- The Plan-Do-Check-Act (PDCA) Cycle of systematic process improvement. (See *The Problem Solving Memory Jogger*™ for details.)

- How to create a process flowchart. (See pages 36–44 of *The Problem Solving Memory Jogger*™ for details.)

- How to build and use shadow boards (see Glossary). This technique enables you to organize and store your tools and equipment in the most effective manner possible.

- Error-proofing techniques. (See chapter 5, "Error Proofing," for details.)

filtration 4il'tefən] n. 过滤

How to do it [TEAM]

You use the PDCA Cycle to make improvements to your setup and changeover processes. The specific steps involved in this procedure are outlined on the next several pages.

1. Evaluate your current processes. **(Plan)**

   a. Conduct an overview of your current production process to identify all equipment and processes that require downtime for changeover. Include all processes that require tooling replacement or new dies, patterns, molds, paints, test equipment, filtration media, and so on.

   b. Collect data using a check sheet for each process. Make sure the check sheet includes information about the following:

   • Duration of the changeover. This is the time it takes from the start of the changeover process to its completion, including preparation and cleanup.

   • The amount of production typically lost during the changeover, including number of units not produced, number of hours that operators are not engaged in productive activities, lost production time, and rework (measured in hours and units).

   • Process events that are _constraint_ operations: these are operations that are long in duration or are critical to completing the manufacturing process.

   c. Create a matrix diagram (see the next page) to display this data for each production process (categories might include setup time, resources and materials required, and changeover time).

A Sample Matrix Diagram

Data-Collection Matrix Diagram				
Information Collected By	Process Name/ No.	Setup Time	Resources/ Materials Required	Changeover Time

  d. Select a process as your target for improvement. A
      good process to choose is one that has a long down-
      time, setup time, and/or changeover time; is a fre-
      quent source of error or safety concerns; or is critical
      to process output.

   Tip A constraint operation that requires a
      changeover during your production operations
      is often a good first target to select. Choose no
      more than three targets to work on at one time.

2. Document all the current changeover activities for
   the process you have selected. **(Plan)**

   a. Make a checklist of all the parts and steps required
      in the current changeover, including the following:

      • Names
      • Specifications
      • Numeric values for all measurements and
        dimensions

- Part numbers
- Special settings

b. Identify any waste or problems associated with your current changeover activities.

c. Record the duration of each activity. See the sample data sheet below.

Quick-Changeover Data Sheet				
OP#: 20 Machine Shell		Team Members: Julie, Ben, Chris, Elise, Erik		
Step #	Element	Time (minutes)	Elapsed Time (minutes)	Notes
10	Assemble cutting inserts	5	5	Inserts are not kitted to match the number of spindles. There are twelve spindles.
20	Move inserts to machine	10	15	Inserts kept in central store on other side of plant.
30	Remove old inserts	10	25	Old inserts must be logged in by spindle number.
40	Install inserts using sleeve positioner tool	30	55	Start new tool wear SPC chart.
50	Run twelve pieces for first piece inspection	5	60	Samples sent to quality for full dimensional check.

d. Create a graph of your current changeover time (in seconds) to establish a baseline for improvement.

e. Set your improvement target. A target of a 50% reduction is recommended.

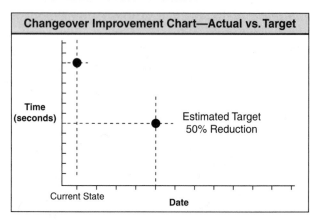

Changeover Improvement Chart—Actual vs. Target

Time (seconds)

Estimated Target 50% Reduction

Current State

Date

3. Identify internal and external process activities. **(Plan)**

a. Create two categories on your checklist: one for internal processes, and one for external processes.

b. List each task under the appropriate category, making sure to keep the tasks in the correct sequence.

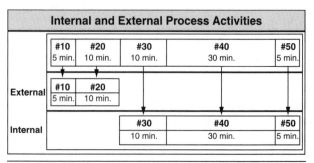

Internal and External Process Activities

	#10 5 min.	#20 10 min.	#30 10 min.	#40 30 min.	#50 5 min.
External	#10 5 min.	#20 10 min.			
Internal			#30 10 min.	#40 30 min.	#50 5 min.

4. Turn as many internal processes as possible into external processes. **(Plan)**

Using your checklist, complete the following steps:

a. Identify the activities that employees currently perform while the line or process is idle that can be performed while it is still running.

b. Identify ways to prepare in advance any operating conditions that must be in place while the line is running (e.g., preheating equipment).

c. Standardize parts and tools that are required for the changeover process, including the following:

- Dimensions.

- Securing devices used.

- Methods of locating and centering objects.

- Methods of <u>expelling</u> and clamping objects.

5. Streamline the process. **(Plan)**

a. Use visual management techniques (see chapter 4 for details) to organize your workplace.

b. Consider ways to error-proof the process.

c. Consider ways to eliminate unnecessary delays in your internal processes by doing the following:

- Identifying the activities that can be done <u>concurrently</u> by multiple employees.

- Using signals, such as buzzers or whistles, to cue operators.

- Using one-turn, one-motion, or interlocking methods.

d. Consider ways to eliminate unnecessary delays in your external processes by making improvements in the following:

- Storage and transportation of parts and tools.

feasibility • Automation methods.

[fiza'bılətı] • Accessibility of resources.

敏捷性 e. Create a new process map showing your proposed
(可行性) changes to the setup process.

6. Test your proposed changes to the process. **(Do)**

a. Consider the <u>feasibility</u> of each proposed change.

calibrate b. Prepare and check all materials and tools required
['kælə,breit] for changeover. Make sure they are where they
v. 校准-测量仪 should be and that they are in good working order.

器, 使... 标准 c. Perform your revised setup activities for the parts
and tools. Adjust settings, <u>calibrate</u> equipment,
set checkpoints, and so on, as required.

d. Perform a trial run of your proposed changes.

e. Collect data on the duration of the setup time,
and update your changeover improvement chart.

7. Evaluate the results of your changes. **(Check)**

Take a look at the results of the changes you have
made. Did the results meet your target goal? If so,
go on to step 8. If not, make adjustments or consider
other ways in which you can streamline your
changeover activities and make the process external.

8. Implement your new quick-changeover process and
continue to work to improve it. **(Act)**

• Document the new procedures and train all
involved employees on the new procedures.

• Continue to collect data for continuous
improvement of the changeover process.

• Create a revised matrix diagram of the change
processes (see step 1, item c) and begin the quick-
changeover process again.

Chapter 7

Standard Operations

What are standard operations?

In a lean enterprise, a *work combination* is a mixture of people, processes, materials, and technology that comes together to enable the completion of a work process. The term *standard operations* refers to the most efficient work combination that a company can put together.

What do they do?

When you apply all your knowledge of lean principles to a particular work process to make it as efficient as possible, a standard operation is the result. Employees then use this documented process as a guide to consistently apply the tasks they must perform in that work process.

In addition, once you prepare standard operations for your work processes, they serve as the basis for all your organization's training, performance-monitoring, and continuous-improvement activities.

Why use them?

As discussed in previous chapters of this book, a big part of making your organization a lean enterprise is identifying different types of waste and finding ways to eliminate them. Ultimately, however, it is the correct combination of people, processes, materials, and technology that enables your organization to create quality products and services at the lowest possible operational cost.

definable [dɪˈfaɪnəbl] adj. 可下定义的

Putting together standard operations forces you to break down each of your work processes into definable elements. This enables you to readily identify waste, develop solutions to problems, and provide all employees with guidance about the best way to get things done.

Many organizations that have used standard operations report that this lean initiative is the one that has had the biggest impact on their ability to produce better-quality products and services, make their work flow smoother, and make their training process more productive. In addition, standard operations enable employees to actually see the waste that they previously didn't see.

How do I develop standard operations for my organization? LEADER

The process for developing standard operations involves eight steps (listed below). A big part of this process involves gathering information about how your organization's work processes should be done.

1. Establish improvement teams.

2. Determine your takt time.

3. Determine your cycle time.

4. Determine your work sequence.

5. Determine the standard quantity of your work in progress.

6. Prepare a standard workflow diagram.

7. Prepare a standard operations sheet.

8. Continuously improve your standard operations.

The remainder of this chapter discusses these eight steps in detail.

---

insight +into
(ˌɪnˈsaɪt) 理解.
coord
coordinate
(koˈɔrdnˌmeɪ) 合作

Step 1: Establish improvement teams

Some organizations take a top-down approach to the development of standard operations: supervisors alone determine what work tasks are to be performed, by whom, and when. Other organizations believe that only front-line workers should develop standard operations because these employees have a keen insight into how things are done.

But due to the nature of the steps required to establish standard operations, a team-based approach is best. It is best to have all employees who are impacted by a work process involved in the development of standard operations for that process. Lean organizations understand the need for complete buy-in and support of all work tasks by all the employees involved. It's also important to coordinate this team effort with your organization's other lean initiatives.

Step 2: Determine your takt time

Takt time is the total available work time per day (or shift), divided by customer-demand requirements per day (or shift). Takt time enables your organization to balance the pace of its production outputs to match the rate of customer demand. The mathematical formula for determining your takt time is as follows:

$$\text{takt time} = \frac{\text{available daily production time}}{\text{required daily quantity of output}}$$

Step 3: Determine your cycle time

Cycle time is the time it takes to successfully complete the tasks required for a work process. It is important to note that a work process's cycle time may or may not equal its takt time.

The process capacity table is a helpful tool for gathering information about the sequence of operations that make up a work process and the time required to complete each operation. Ultimately, the process capacity table can help you determine machine and operator capacity.

Handwritten margin notes:

wear
[wεr]
磨損

summation
[sʌmˈeʃən] 統和

Steps for Creating a Process Capacity Table

1. Enter part number for which capacity is being calculated.

2. Enter line/cell name.

3. Enter *net operating time per shift*. Total minutes less allowances for known time when machines or operators are unavailable to perform necessary tasks (e.g., preventive maintenance, operators' breaks).

4. Enter the number of shifts.

5. Record the maximum output per shift. Hint: Established by the lowest throughput operation.

6. Enter *finished component/product cycle time*. Cycle time = available production time/maximum output per shift.

7. Enter *required output per shift*. Output required for meeting customer demand.

8. Enter Takt time. Takt time = available production time/required quantity.

9. Enter date of capacity calculation.

10. Enter the number of pages of process capacity table.

11. Enter name of individual/team that prepared the process capacity table.

12. Enter the sequence number of each processing step being performed on the part or product.

13. Record the operation description, which is the process being performed on the part or product.

14. Enter the number (if applicable) of the machine performing the process.

15. Enter the *manual time*. Time an operator takes to manually operate a machine when an automatic cycle is not activated; includes the time required to unload a finished part, load a new part, and restart the machine.

16. Record the *automated time*. Time required for a machine's automatic cycle to perform an operation, from when the start button is activated to when the finished part is ready to be unloaded.

17. Calculate the *total cycle time* by adding the manual time and the automated time.

18. Enter the pieces per change, the total number of parts or products that a machine typically produces before its tool bits must be changed due to wear.

19. Record the *change time*. Amount of time required to physically change a machine's tool bits or perform a sample inspection (i.e., time required to change tooling due to normal wear during a production run—not the change-over time required to go from one part or product to making another).

20. Calculate the *time per piece*, the change time divided by the pieces per change.

21. To calculate the *production capacity per shift* divide available production time by the summation of total cycle time and time per piece for a one-piece-flow operation. For a batch operation, divide the available production time by the summation of the cycle time and the time per piece for the constraining operation. Note: Example cited is based on a batch operation with a constraining operation.

Process Capacity Table

Part No.	Line/Cell Name	Net Operating Time/Shift	# of Shifts	Maximum Output per Shift	Cycle Time	Required Output per Shift	Takt Time	Prepared by
80-904212	Shell Mfg.– Batch Operations	480 min. less 5 min. for PM each shift = 475 min.	2	5,619	5.07 sec.	4,800	5.9375 sec.	H. Hopper–Operator

Date: ____ Page __ of __

Step	Operation Description	Machine No.	Processing Time			Tool Change Time			Production Capacity per Shift
			Manual	Auto	Total Cycle	Pieces per Change	Change Time	Time per Piece	
10	Cut Bar Stock	C1	—	1 sec.	1 sec.	150,000	5 min.	0.002 sec.	28,443
20	Machine Shell (*Constraining Operations*)	M1	—	5 sec.	5 sec.	50,000	60 min.	0.072 sec.	5,619
30	Thread Shell	T1	—	2 sec.	2 sec.	75,000	60 min.	0.048 sec.	13,916
40	Weld Side Wire	W1	—	1 sec.	1 sec.	150,000	5 min.	0.002 sec.	28,443

sequential
[sɪ'kwɛnʃəlɪ]
adj. 连续的

convey
[kən've]
v. 运送

conveyer
[kən've]
运输装置

Tip Complete a process capacity table *before* you begin making changes such as moving equipment, changing the sequence of your operations, or moving employees' positions and/or changing their job responsibilities. It is important to first know what your current capacity is and what it will be in the new process configuration that you plan.

Step 4: Determine your work sequence

A *work sequence* is the sequential order in which the tasks that make up a work process are performed. A work sequence provides employees with the correct order in which to perform their duties. This is especially important for multifunction operators who must perform tasks at various workstations within the takt time.

A standard operations combination chart enables your improvement team to study the work sequence for all your organization's work processes. In such a chart, each task is listed sequentially and broken down into manual, automated, wait, and walk times.

Wait time is not included in a process capacity table because worker idle time has no impact on automated activities or the capacity of a process. However, wait time is included in a standard operations combination chart to identify idle time during which a worker could instead be performing other tasks, such as external setup, materials handling, or inspection. The goal is to eliminate all worker idle time.

Standard Operations Combination Chart

Standard Operations Combination Chart

Date: 10/02		Page 1 of 1	
Operator: R. Smith		Prepared by: R. Smith	

Item/Part No./ Name: Resistor Powder	Process: Mixing	Machine: Mixer Dryer Screener	Cell: Line 1	Required Output: 600#/shift	Takt Time: 240 min.
				Cycle Time: 1250	Gap: 1010 min.

Step	Operation Description	Time Manual	Time Auto	Time Walk	Time Wait
1	Retrieve raw materials	15		5	
2	Weigh materials	20			
3	Position materials	5		5	
4	Load materials	5			
5	Mix materials		90		90
6	Verify consistency	5			
7	Convey materials to dryer		10		
8	Dry powder		60		60
9	Screen powder		60		10
10	Load drums	5			
11	Dispose of unacceptable material	5		10	
12	Test Materials	30	30	25	990
	Totals	90	250	45	1050

Operation Cycle Time

Manual: ——
Auto: - - - -
Walk: ～～～
Wait: ↕

(horizontal axis: 25 50 75 100 125 150 175 200 225 250 ...)
(upper axis: 1175 1200 1225 1250)

The steps for completing a standard operations combination chart are described below.

1. At the top of a form like the one shown on page 69, indicate the following:

   a. The date that the work process is being mapped.

   b. The number of pages (if the chart is more than one page long).

   c. The name of the equipment operator.

   d. The name of the person entering data on the form (if different from the operator).

   e. The number and/or name of the part or product being produced.

   f. The name of the process or activity being mapped.

   g. The machine number and/or name.

   h. The work cell number and/or name.

   i. The required output per designated period (e.g., parts per shift or pounds per day).

   j. The takt time for the process.

   k. The total capacity for the process (see step 3). Ideally, this should equal the takt time that you calculated in step 2.

2. The difference between the takt time and the cycle time (see step 3) for the work process.

3. It is often helpful to indicate the type of units the work activity is usually measured in. Activities are normally measured in seconds, but some are measured in minutes or even longer intervals.

4. Number every fifth or tenth line on the graph area to facilitate your recording of activity times. Choose convenient time intervals so that either the takt time or the actual cycle time—whichever is greater—is located near the right side of the graph area.

appropriate [ə'proprɪ,et] adj 適當的

5. Draw a line that represents the activity's takt time. Trace the line with red so it stands out.

6. Sequentially number each operational step in the appropriate column. Steps can include any or all of the following:

   a. Manual operations.

   horizontal ['harəzɑntl]
   水平的

   b. Automated operations.

   vertical ['vɜtɪkl]

   c. Time spent walking from one location to another.

   correspond [,kɔrɪ'spɑnd]
   v. 符合, 一致

   d. Time spent waiting.

7. Provide a brief name and description for each step.

8. Note the time required for the completion of each step in the appropriate column.

9. Draw a horizontal line on the graph representing each step, using the following guidelines:

   a. The length of the line should equal the duration of the step.

   b. The line type should match the action type (see the line key at the top of the sample chart).

   c. Each line type should be in a different color, which will make your chart much easier to read.

   d. Each line you draw should begin at the point on the vertical time line that corresponds to the actual time the activity begins. It should end at the actual time the activity ends.

For example, if the first step of a work activity is an automatic hopper fill that takes fifteen seconds to complete, and the operator assembles a carton for ten seconds during that fifteen seconds, both steps would start at time zero, with the carton assembly ending at time ten and the automatic fill ending at time fifteen.

However, if the operator waits until the automatic hopper fill is completed before assembling the carton, the fill would start at time zero and end at time ten, but the carton assembly would start at time fifteen and end at time twenty-five.

Your completed standard operations combination chart should provide you with some useful insights, including the following:

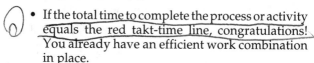

- If the total time to complete the process or activity equals the red takt-time line, congratulations! You already have an efficient work combination in place.

- If the total time required to complete the process or activity falls short of the red takt-time line, you might be able to add other operations to the activity to use your resources more effectively.

- If the total time required to complete the process or activity is longer than the red takt-time line, there is waste in your process.

Use the following steps to identify where this waste occurs:

1. Look over the steps in your process to see if any of them can be compressed or eliminated. Perhaps one or more steps can be completed during periods when the equipment operator is waiting for automated operations to be completed.

2. Look at the movement of employees and materials. Can you reduce or eliminate any of it by relocating supplies or equipment?

synchronize [ˈsɪŋkrənaɪz] v. 同时发生

Step 5: Determine the standard quantity of your work in progress

The standard quantity of your work in progress (WIP) is the minimum amount of WIP inventory that must be held at or between your work processes. Without having this quantity of completed work on hand, it is impossible to <u>synchronize</u> your work operations.

When determining the best standard quantity of WIP you should have, consider the following points:

- Try to keep the quantity as small as possible.
- Ensure that the quantity you choose is suitable to cover the time required for your error-proofing and quality-assurance activities.
- Make sure that the quantity enables all employees to easily and safely handle parts and materials between work operations.

For more information on establishing inventory levels, see chapter 9, "The Kanban System."

Step 6: Prepare a standard workflow diagram

A *workflow diagram* shows your organization's current equipment layout and the movement of materials and workers during work processes. Such a diagram helps your improvement team plan future improvements to your organization, such as one-piece flow (see chapter 8, "One-Piece Flow," for details).

supplement [ˈsʌpləmənt] n. 补充

The information in your workflow diagram <u>supplements</u> the information in your process capacity table and standard operations combination chart. When combined, the data in these three charts serves as a good basis for developing your standard operations sheet (see step 7).

precaution [prɪ'kɔʃən] 預防措施
adjacent [ə'dʒesənt] 附近臨的 (next to)

The steps for completing a workflow diagram are described below.

Workflow Diagram Steps

1. At the top of the diagram, indicate the following:
   a. The beginning and end points of the activity you are mapping.
   b. The date the activity is being mapped. The name of the person completing the diagram should also be included.
   c. The name and/or number of the part or product being produced.

2. Sketch the work location for the work process you are mapping, showing all of the facilities directly involved with the process.

3. Indicate the work sequence by numbering the facilities in the order in which they are used during the activity.

4. Connect the facility numbers with solid arrows and number them, starting with 1 and continuing to the highest number needed. Use solid arrows to indicate the direction of the workflow.

5. Using a dashed arrow, connect the highest-numbered facility to facility number 1. This arrow indicates a return to the beginning of the production cycle.

6. Place a diamond symbol (◇) at each facility that requires a quality check.   asterisk [ˈæstərɪsk] 星号

7. Place a cross symbol (†) at each facility where safety precautions or checks are required. Pay particular attention to facilities that include rotating parts, blades, or pinch points.

8. Place an asterisk (✳) at each location where it is normal to accumulate standard WIP inventory. Adjacent to the asterisk, indicate the magnitude of the inventory—measured in number, weight, volume, and so on.

9. Also enter the total magnitude of the inventory in the "Number of WIP Pieces" box.

10. Enter the takt time for the operation in the "Takt Time" box. Calculate the takt time using the mathematical formula shown in "Step 2: Determine your takt time" earlier in this chapter.

11. Enter the time required to complete a single cycle of the activity in the "Cycle Time" box. Ideally, this time should equal the takt time.

The workflow diagram provides a visual map of workspace organization, movement of materials and workers, and distances traveled—information not included in either the process capacity table or the standard operations combination chart. You can use this information to improve your workspace organization, re-sequence your work steps, and reposition your equipment, materials, and workers to shorten your cycle time and the overall travel distance. This will help you to achieve your takt time.

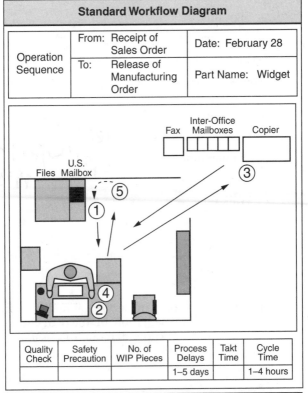

	Standard Workflow Diagram	
Operation Sequence	From: Receipt of Sales Order	Date: February 28
	To: Release of Manufacturing Order	Part Name: Widget

Quality Check	Safety Precaution	No. of WIP Pieces	Process Delays	Takt Time	Cycle Time
			1–5 days		1–4 hours

Step 7: Prepare a standard operations sheet

Numerous formats exist for standard operations sheets. In general, the layout for your sheet should include the components listed below:

- The header section should contain the following:
  - Process name
  - Part or product name
  - Takt time
  - Cycle time
  - Sign-offs
  - Approval date
  - Revision level

- The work sequence section should contain the following:
  - Sequence number
  - Description of task
  - Manual time
  - Automated time
  - Walk time
  - Inventory requirements
  - Key points
  - Safety precautions
  - Related job procedures

- The workflow diagram section should contain a pictorial representation of the work area. (Refer to the workflow diagram discussion in step 6 for details.)

[handwritten annotation: precaution [prɪ'kɔʃən] n 預防 措施]

- The footer section should contain the following:
  - Lean enterprise tools applied to the work process
  - Safety equipment required
  - Page indicator (for multiple-page standard operations sheets)

The layout of a standard operations sheet is straightforward. See the sample below.

Standard Operations Sheet					
Header:					Workflow Diagram
Work Sequence Information gathered from process capacity table and standard operations combination chart:					
#	Description	Time	Inventory	Safety/Other	
Footer:					

Step 8: Continuously improve your standard operations

After you complete your standard operations sheet, you should train all employees who are affected by your changes to the work process in question. Don't be surprised if, during this training, employees discover potential opportunities for even greater improvement.

It is through the continuous improvement of your standard operations that your organization can systematically drive out waste and reduce costs. You should review your organization's standard operations sheet(s) on a periodic basis to ensure all employees are accurately complying with them.

Chapter 8
One-Piece Flow

What is it?

One-piece flow is the movement of products through the manufacturing process one unit at a time. This is in contrast to batch processing (also known as large-lot processing), which produces a large number of identical units at once and sends all of them to each operation in the production process together.

对比 contrast

What does it do?

One-piece flow focuses employees' efforts on the manufacturing process itself rather than on waiting, transporting products, and storing inventory. It also makes the production process flow smoothly, one piece at a time, creating a steady workload for all employees involved.

Why use it?

There are many advantages to incorporating the one-piece-flow method into your work processes. These include the following:

* It reduces the time that elapses between a customer order and shipment of the finished product.

* It prevents the wait times and production delays that can occur during batch processing.

* By reducing excess inventory, one-piece flow reduces the labor, energy, and space that employees must devote to storing and transporting large lots or batches.

devote [dɪ'vot] v. 将~奉献给

- It reduces the damage that can occur to product units during batch processing.

- It reveals any defects or problems in product units early in the production process.

- It gives your organization the flexibility to meet customer demands for a specific product at a specific time.

- It reduces your operating costs by making non-value-added work more evident. This enables you to eliminate waste.

What are the requirements for using the one-piece-flow method?

One-piece flow works best when your production process and products meet certain requirements. One is that your product changeover times must be very short; almost instantaneous is best. One-piece flow is impractical when many time-consuming changeover operations are needed during the production process.

Another requirement is that the products you make must be suitable for one-piece flow. Very small product units are usually not suitable because too much time is required for their setup, positioning, and removal from production equipment.

One-piece flow might be possible for the production of very small product units if you can completely automate their movement through your production process and if your cycle time (see Glossary) is short.

Case example: Quick-Lite implements one-piece flow

Quick-Lite is a <u>hypothetical</u> company that produces spark plugs. One of the spark-plug components that Quick-Lite produces is the shell, which is the threaded part of the spark plug that is screwed into the engine.

Manufacturing a spark-plug shell involves four basic operations, as shown in the table below.

Operation	Cycle Time (seconds)
10 – Cut bar stock	1
20 – Machine shell	5
30 – Cut threads	2
40 – Weld side wire	1

Each of these four operations in Quick-Lite's batch process handles 1000 spark-plug shells before placing them into storage to wait for the next operation. The shells are stored for one hour after each operation.

The time required for Quick-Lite to manufacture 1000 spark-plug shells during its batch-processing method is calculated as follows:

Batch-Processing Method Calculation			
Operation	No. of Pieces	Cycle Time (seconds)	Total Time (seconds)
10	1000	1	1000
Storage delay			3600
20	1000	5	5000
Storage delay			3600
30	1000	2	2000
Storage delay			3600
40	1000	1	1000
Total Time (seconds):			19,800

In a one-piece-flow method, as soon as one piece is finished, it is immediately moved and processed by the next operation. In such a manufacturing process, the constraining operation (see Glossary) is the one that limits the output rate of finished parts. In this case, the constraining operation is Operation 20.

Bar stock is cut (Operation 10) one second before it is required by Operation 20. Operation 30 begins only after the completion of Operation 20. Therefore, the lead time (see Glossary) for the first unit is nine seconds. Each subsequent unit comes off the production line every five seconds. Because all storage delays are eliminated, the total time to produce units 2 through 1000 is 4995 seconds.

Thus, the time required for Quick-Lite to manufacture 1000 spark plugs with a one-piece-flow method is just 5004 seconds (4995 + 9), compared to the 19,800 seconds required with a batch-processing method.

Using one-piece flow enables Quick-Lite to reduce its overall production time by about 75%. Real-world manufacturing operations that convert to the one-piece-flow method often show similar results.

How do I coordinate my production cycle time with my customer orders?

The number of units you produce should equal the number of items your customers order. In other words, your selling cycle time should equal your manufacturing cycle time.

Case example: Quick-Lite coordinates its cycle time with customer orders

Quick-Lite's customer, an automobile manufacturer, places an order for 9600 spark plugs to be delivered every day. The one-piece-flow production line is available for 16 hours (57,600 seconds) each day. Quick-Lite can fill the order by producing one spark-plug shell every six seconds (57,600 ÷ 9600 = 6).

Since the line is capable of producing one shell every five seconds, Quick-Lite can fill the order in 48,000 seconds (5 × 9600 = 48,000), leaving 9000 seconds (150 minutes) for other activities, such as shift changeover, total productive maintenance (see chapter 10 for details), and individual or team improvement.

> **Tip** Don't be tempted to overproduce. Some companies produce extra quantities of their products in an effort to maximize the use of their machines. Before you decide to produce surplus inventory, first consider the costs of over-production and maintaining an inventory.

What is the difference between a push system and a pull system?

"Fat" organizations use a *push system*. In such a system, goods are produced and handed off to a downstream process, where they are stored until needed. This type of system creates excess inventory.

Lean organizations, on the other hand, use a *pull system*, in which goods are built only when a downstream process requests them. The customer then "pulls" the product from the organization.

The final operation in a production process drives a pull system. Customer-order information goes only to the product's final assembly area. As a result, nothing is produced until it is needed or wanted downstream, so the organization produces only what is needed.

A pull system streamlines the flow of materials through your production process. This greatly improves your organization's productivity by doing the following:

- It reduces the time that employees spend in non-value-added steps, such as waiting and transporting product units.

- It reduces downtime caused by product changeovers and equipment adjustments.

- It reduces the distances that materials or works in progress must travel between assembly steps.

- It eliminates the need for inspection or reworking of materials.

- It bases your equipment usage on your cycle time.

Case example: Quick-Lite deals with over-capacity

One of Quick-Lite's threading machines can thread twelve spark-plug shells at a time. Quick-Lite purchased this machine several years ago to increase throughput.

When shell types are changed, twelve spindles must be set up on this machine. Once set up, it can produce twelve threaded shells every two seconds. But because Quick-Lite's customer requires only one threaded shell every six seconds, this machine creates an over-capacity that does not improve operations; it just builds up excess inventory.

Case example: Quick-Lite deals with under-capacity

If Quick-Lite has only one eight-hour shift (28,000 seconds) to produce all 9600 spark plugs it needs to deliver each day, it must produce shells at a rate of one every three seconds ($28,000 \div 9600 = 3$) to fill the order. But the company's current operations can produce at a rate of only one shell every five seconds. How can Quick-Lite fill this order in one shift?

Answer: Only one of the four operations in the process doesn't meet the three-second requirement: Operation 20, the constraining operation. To fill this order in one shift, Quick-Lite can either add additional capacity to this operation or, if possible, speed up the operation or break it up into multiple operations.

What is the best type of equipment for one-piece flow?

To accommodate one-piece flow, equipment should be correctly sized to meet customer demand. Machines designed for batch production might not be easy to adapt to one-piece-flow cycle times.

One-piece flow works best with machines that are smaller and somewhat slower than equipment that is suited for batch processing. Equipment used for one-piece flow also needs to be easy to set up quickly so that you can use it to produce a wide mix of products.

Because the volume, capacity, and force requirements are often lower for one-piece-flow production, machines that are suited for it can be smaller. Smaller machines save space and leave little opportunity for waste, such as inventory and defective parts, to accumulate. They are also less expensive to purchase.

Slower machines are often sufficient for one-piece flow because the aim is to produce goods according to the manufacturing cycle time.

Automated and semi-automated machines work well in one-piece-flow production. They stop and give the operator a signal when a cycle is complete or if any problems occur. They are sometimes also capable of notifying the next operation when to begin processing. And they often unload automatically after processing is done.

> **Tip** Synchronize your equipment's production operations by delaying the start of faster operations rather than speeding up or slowing down the machines. Running production equipment outside of its specified range can reduce product quality or tool life.

Case example: Quick-Lite chooses appropriate machines

To fill Quick-Lite's order, Operation 30 needs to perform at a cycle time equal to that of Operation 20: one part every five seconds. But the throughput of Operation 30's multi-spindle machine is twelve parts every two seconds.

To implement one-piece-flow, Quick-Lite must synchronize the equipment used for Operations 20 and 30 to produce at the customer takt time.

Rather than using the multi-spindle machine, the team at Quick-Lite decides to use a smaller in-line threading machine that operates at a cycle time of one part every five seconds. This allows them to avoid extra setup time and overproduction.

The Quick-Lite team also decides that automating their machinery will work well because each operation in the production process has a different cycle time. Thus, when Operation 20, shell machining, is at the four-second mark, it signals Operation 10, bar-stock cutting, to perform its task.

How do I prepare my work areas and employee training for one-piece flow?

To achieve a one-piece-flow method's full potential, it is important to follow five points with regard to your work-cell layout and employee training. These points are outlined below.

1. Simplify the flow of your materials and parts. Below are several guidelines to follow:

    -   Keep all goods flowing in the same direction.

    -   Make sure all parts flow from storage through the factory according to the processing sequence.

- Use first-in, first-out, or FIFO (see Glossary), stocking.

- Arrange parts for easy feeding into the production line.

- Eliminate any non-value-added space in your work cells.

- Keep all pathways in work areas clear; leave aisles open along walls and windows.

- Make sure that material input and production output are separate operations.

- Position your equipment to allow easy maintenance access.

- Make sure separate work processes are located as close together as possible.

2. Set up your production lines to maximize the equipment operators' productivity. Review the feasibility of both straight-line and U-shaped work cells and their impact on both operator movement and productivity and the flow of work materials.

   Remember that a U-shaped work cell brings the ending point of a work process close to the beginning point, which minimizes the distance an operator has to move before beginning a new production cycle. This setup is better for some work processes than a straight-line work cell.

3. Allot space in the layout of your work cells for regular equipment and product inspection. Remember that the employees working in each cell must be able to easily conduct a full-lot inspection. Such inspections prevent defects by catching any errors and non-standard conditions. This ensures that only defect-free parts are fed to the next step in your production process.

---

4. Minimize your in-process inventory. Predetermine the stock that employees will have on hand for the entire production line. Arrange your work cells to enable an easy flow of materials into and out of all work areas.

5. When your equipment is arranged to enable a smooth process flow, equipment operators might need to learn how to run different types of equipment. Such operators usually need to work standing up, instead of sitting down, so they can easily run a number of machines in sequence. Keep this in mind when designing your work cells.

   Cross-train your employees so that they know how to perform different work functions. Equipment operators are then able to go to other work cells if production is not required at their normal work areas. This also enables an entire work team to take full responsibility for the production process.

What tools should I be familiar with to implement a one-piece-flow process?

Three tools are necessary for assessing and planning for a one-piece-flow process:

1. PQ analysis table

2. Process route table

3. Workflow diagram

These tools are explained below.

PQ analysis table

A *PQ analysis table* is a tool that helps employees understand the types of products your organization produces and the volume that your customers demand. It also shows whether the majority of your production volume is made up of a small or wide variety of parts.

©2002 GOAL/QPC

The PQ analysis table enables employees to identify what products are suitable for one-piece-flow production. (The *P* in *PQ* stands for *products*; the *Q* stands for *quantity* of production output.)

Case example: Quick-Lite's PQ analysis

Quick-Lite conducts a PQ analysis of its spark-plug final-assembly part numbers to see if a wide or limited variety of spark plugs makes up most of the volume. They find that six spark plugs made up 53.3% of the total volume. The manufacturing processes for these six spark plugs are likely candidates for one-piece-flow operations. (See the graphic below.)

PQ Analysis					
No.	Part No.	Quantity	Cumulative Total	%	Cumulative %
1	80-904212	20,190,000	20,190,000	16.2	16.2
2	90-801234	15,230,000	35,420,000	12.2	28.3
3	80-903123	10,200,000	45,620,000	8.2	36.5
4	80-902123	7,900,000	53,520,000	6.3	42.8
5	80-901123	7,400,000	60,920,000	5.9	48.7
6	89-801234	5,670,000	66,590,000	4.5	53.3
		66,590,000	282,260,000		

Once the Quick-Lite team identifies these products in a PQ analysis table, they create a process route table to determine whether a similar technology is used to manufacture all six types of spark plugs.

What is a process route table, and how do I use one?

A *process route table* shows the machines and equipment required for processing a component or completing an assembly process. Such a table helps you to arrange your equipment in production lines according to product type and to group related manufacturing tasks into work cells. You can also use a process route table to analyze process, function, or task-level activities.

The steps for creating a process route table are as follows:

1. Somewhere above the top of the table, write the following:

   a. The name or number of the department whose activity is being analyzed.

   b. The operation or product that is being analyzed.

   c. The name of the person completing the form.

   d. The date on which the form is completed.

2. Use the "No." column on the left for the sequential numbering of the products or operations being analyzed.

3. For each product or operation you are analyzing, enter the item name, machine number, or function.

4. For each product or operation, enter circled numbers in the various resource columns that correspond to the sequence in which the resources are used for that product or operation.

5. Connect the circled numbers with lines or arrows to indicate the sequence of operations.

Once you have completed the table, look for items or products that follow the same, or nearly the same, sequence of machine and/or resource usage. You might be able to group these machines and/or resources together in the same work cells to improve the efficiency of your operations. (See the sample process route table below.)

Process Route Table								
No.	Part No.	Process Name						
		Cut	Machine	Machine	Machine	Thread	Thread	Weld	Weld
		Machine No.							
		C1	M1	M2	M3	T1	T2	W1	W2
1	80-904212	①	②			③		④	
2	90-801234	①		②			③		④
3	80-903123	①	②			③		④	
4	80-902123	①	②			③		④	
5	80-901123	①			②		③		④
6	89-801234	①			②		③		④

Before you begin rearranging your equipment and work cells to accommodate a one-piece-flow method, be sure to create a process capacity table to analyze your current machine and employee capacity. (See chapter 7, "Standard Operations," for details about creating a process capacity table.)

What are the final steps?

The next step is to create a *standard operations combination chart*. This chart enables you to study the work sequence for all your organization's work processes. In such a chart, each task is listed sequentially and then broken down into manual, automated, wait, and walk times. (See chapter 7 for details about creating a standard operations combination chart.)

Finally, you should create a *workflow diagram*, which shows your organization's current equipment layout and the movement of materials and workers during your work processes. It helps you identify areas of waste and plan improvements to your work cells that will enable you to implement one-piece-flow production. (See chapter 7 for details about creating a workflow diagram.)

Once your work team a) collects all the data necessary for selecting the products that are suitable for one-piece flow, b) verifies the operations needed and the available capacity, and c) understands the specific task in detail, you can implement the layout of your improved work cells and make one-piece flow a reality in your organization.

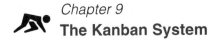

Chapter 9
The Kanban System

What is it?

The kanban system is a method of using cards as visual signals for triggering or controlling the flow of materials or parts during the production process. It synchronizes the work processes within your own organization as well as those that involve your outside suppliers.

What does it do?

In the kanban system, a card (called a kanban) controls the movement of materials and parts between production processes. A kanban moves with the same materials all the way down the production line. When a process needs more parts or materials, it sends the corresponding kanban to the supplier; the card acts as the work order. A kanban card contains the following data:

- What to produce
- How to produce it
- When to produce it
- How much to produce
- How to transport it
- Where to store it

Why use it?

In an ideal world, demand for products would be constant. Organizations could always operate at maximum efficiency, producing exactly what was needed—no more, no less. But for most companies, the amount of work that must be done varies by the day, week, or month.

An organization must have enough capacity so that there are enough people, machines, and materials available to produce what is needed at times of peak demand.

But when there is a smaller amount of work to be done, one of two things can happen: 1) under-utilization of people, machines, or materials or 2) overproduction.

With the kanban system, workers are cross-trained to be knowledgeable about various machines and work processes so that they can work on different manufacturing tasks as needed. This prevents underutilization.

Kanban systems also prevent overproduction, which is the single largest source of waste in most manufacturing organizations. When you use the kanban system correctly, no overproduction will occur.

The kanban system also gives your organization the following positive results:

- All employees always know their production priorities.

- Employees' production directions are based on the current conditions in your workplace.

- Employees are empowered to perform work when and where it is needed. They do not need to wait to be assigned a work task.

- Unnecessary paperwork is eliminated.

- Skill levels among your employees are increased.

What skill and concepts do I need to know?

Before you can put the kanban system in place, you must first make your production process as efficient as possible. Two practices—production smoothing and load balancing—are helpful for doing this.

Production smoothing refers to synchronizing the production of your company's different products to match your customer demand. Once you successfully accomplish production smoothing, daily schedules for your production processes are arranged to ensure production of the required quantity of materials at the required time. Your employees and equipment are all organized toward that end as well.

To successfully do production smoothing, you first break down your required monthly production output into daily units using the following formula:

$$\text{required quantity per day} = \frac{\text{required quantity per month}}{\text{number of days of operation}}$$

Then you compare this daily volume with your operating hours to calculate the *takt time*, which is described in detail in chapter 7, "Standard Operations."

Calculating your takt time for production lets you determine how much to vary the pace of the work you must do.

The mathematical formula for determining your takt time is as follows:

$$\text{takt time} = \frac{\text{available daily production time}}{\text{required daily quantity of output}}$$

Then you look at your *capacity*, which is the ability of a machine and operator to complete the work required,

---

and determine the number of employees required to complete your production processes.

> **Tip** Don't calculate your takt time based on the number of employees already working on your production line. That can result in too much or too little capacity. Instead, calculate your takt time based on the number of units required per day and then determine the number of employees needed to staff the line to produce at that rate.

Load is the volume of work that your organization needs to do. *Load balancing* is finding a balance between the load and your capacity. Timing and volume are critical to achieving load balancing.

> **Tip** Although kanban systems are a very effective way to fine-tune your production levels, they work best only after you have implemented value stream mapping (see chapter 3 for details) and one-piece flow (see chapter 8). This is because kanban systems minimize your stocking levels and use visual management (see chapter 4), error proofing (see chapter 5), and total productive maintenance (see chapter 10) to ensure that quality parts and materials are delivered when a kanban triggers their flow through the production process.

> **Tip** Perform maintenance and process-improvement activities during times of lower demand. This way, during peak demand times, every employee can be actively engaged on the production line.

> **Tip** The kanban system fine-tunes your production process. But it cannot make your organization able to quickly respond to sudden large changes in demand. You might not be able to rally sufficient resources to produce a very big order in time, or to find enough alternate activities to keep employees busy when there is a sudden large drop in orders.

How does the kanban system work?

There are two basic types of kanban cards: *production* kanbans and *withdrawal* kanbans.

A production kanban describes how many of what item a particular operation needs to produce. Once employees have a production kanban in hand, their operation can begin producing the item.

A withdrawal kanban is used to pull items from a preceding operation or a *marketplace*, an area where materials are stocked in a supermarket system. The figure below shows the kanban system in use.

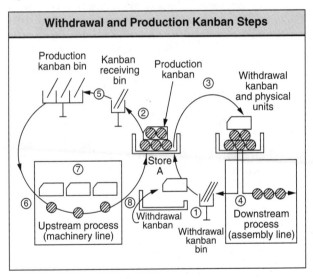

Withdrawal and Production Kanban Steps

Production kanban bin
Kanban receiving bin
Production kanban ③
Withdrawal kanban and physical units
⑤
②
Store A
⑦
⑥
⑧
①
④
Upstream process (machinery line)
Withdrawal kanban
Withdrawal kanban bin
Downstream process (assembly line)

1. An operator from the downstream process brings withdrawal kanbans to the upstream process's marketplace. Each pallet of materials has a kanban attached to it.

---

2. When the operator of the downstream process withdraws the requested items from the marketplace, the production kanban is detached from the pallets of materials and is placed in the kanban receiving bin.

3. For each production kanban that is detached from a pallet of materials, a withdrawal kanban is attached in its place. The two kanbans are then compared for consistency to prevent production errors.

4. When work begins at the downstream process, the withdrawal kanban on the pallet of requested materials is put into the withdrawal kanban bin.

5. At the upstream process, the production kanban is collected from the kanban receiving bin. It is then placed in the production kanban bin in the same order in which it was detached at the marketplace.

6. Items are produced in the same order that their production kanbans arrive in the production bin.

7. The actual item and its kanban must move together when processed.

8. When a work process completes an item, it and the production kanban are placed together in the marketplace so that an operator from the next downstream operation can withdraw them.

   Tip A kanban card should be attached to the actual item it goes with so that it can always be accurately recognized.

What are the general guidelines for using the kanban system?

When using the kanban system, it's important to follow the six general guidelines listed below.

1. An upstream process never sends defective parts to a downstream process.

   a. Operators at a process that produces a defective product must immediately discover it.

   b. The problem(s) that created the defective product must be resolved immediately.

   c. Machines must stop automatically when a defect occurs.

   d. Employees must stop their work operation when a defect occurs.

   e. All defective products mixed with good products must be separated promptly.

   f. Suppliers who ship defective parts to your organization must send the same number of replacement parts in their next shipment. This ensures that the exact number of good parts required is available for production operations.

2. A downstream process withdraws only what it needs from an upstream process.

   a. No withdrawal of materials from a process is allowed without a kanban.

   b. Withdraw the same number of items as kanbans (unless a kanban indicates item quantities of more than one).

   c. A kanban must accompany each item.

3. An upstream process produces the exact quantity of products that will be withdrawn by the next process downstream.

---

a. Inventory must be restricted to an absolute minimum. This is called *just-in-time inventory* (see the next page).

b. Do not produce more items than the number of kanbans (unless a kanban indicates item quantities of more than one).

c. Produce units in the order in which their production kanbans are received.

4. Synchronize your production processes by regularly maintaining your equipment and reassigning workers as needed.

5. Remember that the kanban system is a way of fine-tuning your production amounts.

a. The kanban system cannot easily respond to major changes in production requirements. Your company also needs to have proactive sales and operations-planning procedures in place.

b. The principles of load balancing must be followed.

c. Employees receive work instructions for production and transportation of materials via kanbans only. No other production information is sent to employees.

6. Work to stabilize and improve your production processes. Variations and impractical work methods often produce defective materials. Make sure you keep all your work processes in control, and keep variation levels within the requirements of your customers.

What is a supermarket system, and how do I operate one?

Lean enterprises use a supermarket system to achieve just-in-time inventory. The concept of a supermarket system is similar to that of shopping at a supermarket. When you go to a supermarket, you do the following:

- Select the type and quantity of food you need, taking into account the number of people in your family, the space you have available to store goods, and the number of days the supply must last.

- Put the food items into a shopping cart and pay for them.

When you use a supermarket system for your organization's manufacturing operations, the following steps occur:

- The process that manufactures parts keeps them in a marketplace.

- When the marketplace is full, production stops.

- A downstream process requests parts from an upstream process only when it needs them.

- The responsibility for transporting materials from one process to another belongs to the downstream process that uses them.

A storage area for parts is called a marketplace because it is the place where downstream processes go to get the parts and materials they need.

For a supermarket system to work as efficiently as possible, the following must occur:

- No defective items are sent from a marketplace to downstream processes.

- Marketplaces are assigned the smallest space possible to fit the materials they must hold. A marketplace is clearly defined by a line or divider, and no materials are stored beyond its boundaries.

- A minimum number of items is placed in each marketplace.

- Marketplaces are maintained with visual management techniques. (See chapter 4 for details.)

How do I use the kanban system for an automated assembly line?

To implement the kanban system in an assembly line where no human operators oversee the production equipment, you must make some technical modifications. Automatic limit switches must be installed on your equipment to keep the machines from producing too many units. In addition, all your production processes should be interconnected so that they have the required quantity of standard stock on hand. A fully automatic kanban system is known as an *electric kanban*.

Can I use the kanban system for producing custom orders?

A kanban system is an effective way of controlling the production of specialized parts or products that your organization makes. Using the kanban system for special parts or products ensures the following:

- Your starting and transporting procedures are conducted in the right sequence and on a constant basis.

- You can keep your stocking levels constant. This enables you to reduce your overall stocking levels.

Because companies do not ordinarily produce specialized parts on a regular basis, it's important for

---

employees to share information about their production in a timely manner. Information delays can result in increases or decreases in the number of units you have on hand. Circulating your kanbans more frequently enables you to produce fewer batches of specialized parts more frequently.

How many kanbans should I use?

The number of kanbans you should use depends on the type of inventory-control system you have. There are two types: the *constant order-quantity* system and the *constant order-cycle* system.

With a constant order-quantity system, a downstream process orders a predetermined, fixed quantity of materials from an upstream process whenever inventory levels drop to a predetermined reorder point. This is the quantity level that automatically triggers a new order. Because the order quantity is fixed, the reorder date varies.

A constant order-cycle system, on the other hand, features a fixed reorder date and a varying order quantity. The quantity of materials ordered depends on the amount of materials used since the previous order was placed.

Both types of inventory-control system have pros and cons. Because the number of kanbans used in a constant order-quantity system always stays the same, this type of system makes it easy to error-proof your production operations for these constant, known quantities. Also, it is easy to apply visual management techniques to reflect constant stock levels and use of storage space. However, using a constant order-quantity system increases the complexity of coordinating the movement of materials throughout your plant.

A constant order-cycle system, on the other hand, reduces the complexity of coordinating the movement of materials throughout your plant. This makes this type of system ideal for production systems that use externally supplied parts, where coordinating fixed inbound freight dock times is critical. However, using a constant order-cycle system increases the complexity of managing the number of kanbans in the system because of variable production quantities within a fixed time period. Error-proofing and visual management techniques are also more difficult to use when production quantities vary significantly.

> **Tip** The fewer kanbans you have, the better. Having too many kanbans means you have too much planned inventory. You should monitor and adjust your kanban levels so that you produce only the minimum amount of inventory required to keep your organization's downstream production assets running according to schedule. Too many kanbans, just like excess inventory, can hide problems.

Constant order-quantity system: reorder-point calculation

The reorder point is determined as follows.

- Reorder point:

  average usage during lead time + safety stock − orders placed but not yet received

- Total number of kanbans:

$$\frac{\text{economic lot size} + (\text{daily demand} \times \text{safety coefficient})}{\text{container capacity}}$$

or

$$\frac{\left[\frac{\text{monthly demand}}{\text{monthly number of setups}}\right] + (\text{daily demand} \times \text{safety coefficient})}{\text{container capacity}}$$

Constant order-cycle system: maximum inventory calculation

• Maximum inventory:

daily demand × (order cycle + lead time) + safety stock

Where the order cycle is the time interval between an order time and the next order time, and the lead time is simply the time interval between placing an order and receiving delivery.

• Order cycle:

$$\frac{\text{economic lot size for an expected demand}}{\text{daily average demand}}$$

• the economic lot size (Q) = $\sqrt{\dfrac{2AR}{ic}}$

where A = ordering cost per lot

  R = monthly estimated demand quantity

  i = carrying cost per dollar of an item

  c = unit cost

• Order quantity:

(standard quantity – existing inventory) – (orders placed but not yet received)

• Total number of kanbans:

$$\frac{\text{daily demand} \times (\text{order cycle + lead time + safety period})}{\text{container capacity}}$$

where lead time = processing time + waiting time + conveyance time + kanban collecting time

---

More detailed explanations for the preceding equations are available from many industry sources, including *Toyota Production Systems: An Integrated Approach to Just-In-Time*, Third Edition, by Yashiro Monden (Engineering and Management Press, 1998).

Chapter 10

Total Productive Maintenance

What is it?

Total productive maintenance (TPM) is a series of methods that ensures every piece of equipment in a production process is always able to perform its required tasks so that production is never interrupted. It is a comprehensive, team-based, continuous activity that enhances normal equipment-maintenance activities and involves every worker.

What does it do?

TPM helps you focus on and accelerate the equipment improvements required for you to implement methods such as one-piece flow, quick changeover, and load leveling (see Glossary) as part of your company's lean initiative. TPM also helps to improve your first-time-through, or FTT (see Glossary), quality levels.

Why use it?

Using TPM results in many positive outcomes, including the following:

- Improved equipment performance. Equipment operators and maintenance workers prevent poor performance by conducting maintenance inspections and preventive maintenance activities. They also capture information about poor machine performance, enabling teams to diagnose declining performance and their causes. By preventing and eliminating these causes, these employees can improve performance efficiency.

- Increased equipment availability. TPM enables operators and maintenance workers alike to help prevent equipment failures by performing maintenance inspections and preventive maintenance activities. These employees also capture information regarding machine downtime, enabling your improvement team to diagnose failures and their causes. When you are able to prevent and eliminate the causes of failures, your asset availability improves.

- Increased equipment FTT quality levels. Process parameters that have a direct effect on product quality are called *key control characteristics*. For example, if a thermocouple in a furnace fails and an incorrect measurement is sent to the heating elements, this causes temperatures to fluctuate, which might significantly affect product quality. The goal of a TPM program is to identify these key control characteristics and the appropriate maintenance plan to ensure prevention of a failure of performance degradation.

- Reduced emergency downtime and less need for "firefighting" (i.e., work that must be done in response to an emergency).

- An increased return on investment, or ROI (see Glossary), in equipment.

- Increased employee skill levels and knowledge.

- Increased employee empowerment, job satisfaction, and safety.

How do I implement TPM?

Implementing TPM involves five steps.

1. Improve the effectiveness of your vital equipment.

2. Establish and implement autonomous maintenance.

3. Create a planned maintenance program.

4. Establish an equipment life-cycle management program.

5. Plan for and conduct continuous-improvement activities.

These five steps are described in detail below.

Step 1: Improve the effectiveness of your vital equipment.

The goal of your TPM program is to improve the reliability and performance of each piece of vital equipment in your production processes. *Overall equipment effectiveness* (*OEE*) is a metric that measures three aspects of equipment performance: availability, performance efficiency, and quality rate.

Your equipment must meet its design specifications for each of these three aspects to provide the greatest possible return on your company's investment.

It's important to target the most critical equipment first. Good choices include equipment that performs important processes or that performs marginally.

Once you have selected the equipment to target, you must then calculate the OEE for each machine, as well as the overall OEE of the line, processing unit, or entire plant. (See chapter 11, "Lean Metrics," for more information about calculating OEE.)

OEE is the primary measure of equipment performance. It measures how well your company's capital assets are used. The metric also shows the effect of equipment-related losses. The following seven types of equipment loss are useful ones to track:

1. Downtime due to machine breakdown.

2. Time required for setup and adjustments.

3. Time or cycles lost to inefficient setup.

4. Time or cycles lost to tooling.

5. Time or cycles lost to work stoppages.

6. Operating at less-than-ideal speeds.

7. Producing defective products that are rejected, require rework or repair, or are sold at a lower price.

Set a benchmark of 85% OEE for each piece of equipment. (The goal is usually not 100%; an OEE of 100% would leave no time for planned maintenance downtime or for running a piece of equipment at less than its design performance to avoid overproduction or to synchronize it with other pieces of equipment.) To motivate employees to make improvements, measure the lost revenue and increased costs that result when your equipment operates at a level that falls below this benchmark.

Use a Pareto Chart to display the data you collect; the highest bar on the chart indicates the greatest loss. For details and sample Pareto Charts, see pages 95–104 of *The Memory Jogger™ II*.

Your ultimate goal should be zero defects. Remember that if you can reduce defects to zero for an hour, then it's possible to reduce them to zero for an entire shift, an entire month, or even an entire year!

> **Tip** Make sure that your efforts to improve one OEE variable do not worsen other variables. For instance, don't increase a machine's performance efficiency if the machine will then fail more often or create more defects.

> **Tip** Correlate your OEE with your company's financial indicators. An improvement in OEE

can then be expressed in terms of additional profits or reduced costs, justifying additional capital expenditures.

Case example: Quick-Lite compares its OEE to the benchmark

Quick-Lite is a hypothetical company that manufactures spark plugs. The equipment the company uses to machine its spark-plug shells has the following OEE characteristics:

Availability = 90%

FTT quality = 92%

Performance efficiency = 95%

OEE = 90% × 92% × 95% = 79%

This OEE of 79% does not quite meet the benchmark of 85%.

Step 2: Establish and implement autonomous maintenance.

In autonomous maintenance, equipment operators are trained to assume routine inspection and adjustment tasks normally performed by maintenance staff so that they can share the responsibility for the care of their equipment with the maintenance staff.

When equipment operators perform the routine tasks of maintenance, such as checking, adjusting, and lubricating equipment, maintenance workers are then free to work as analytical problem-solvers. They are able to focus on reliability-centered maintenance and product redesign, which results in permanent improvements.

Autonomous maintenance involves seven elements. They are outlined in the table below.

The Seven Elements of Autonomous Maintenance	
Element	**Purpose**
1. Initial cleaning	• Reduces contamination. • Increases operator's familiarity with equipment and work area. • Uncovers hidden defects.
2. Preventive cleaning measures	• Identifies, isolates, and controls sources of contamination, including leaks, process-related excess, and materials from the external environment.
3. Development of cleaning and lubrication standards	• Combines inspections for cleanliness with lubrication checks so that they can both be performed as efficiently as possible.
4. General inspection	• Conduct torquing, adjustments, and minor calibrations. • Inspect hydraulic, pneumatic, and electrical subsystems.
5. Autonomous inspection	• Equipment operators assume responsibility for lubrication, cleaning, and general inspection of their equipment. • Operators must also be trained with regard to the technical aspects of the equipment.
6. Process discipline	• Improvement of methods and procedures to foster efficiency and repeatability. This has many benefits: 　1. Reduced setup times. 　2. Decreased manufacturing cycle times. 　3. Standardized procedures for handling raw materials. 　4. Visual control and inspection methods.
7. Independent autonomous maintenance	• Self-sustaining improvement.

Tip Before you can implement autonomous maintenance, your equipment operators need to receive basic technical, troubleshooting, and problem-solving training. In addition, maintenance personnel must receive advanced technical training, in addition to training in core trouble-shooting and problem-solving skills.

Maintenance staff or equipment manufacturers can train equipment operators about the basic care of their equipment. Some important tips to teach operators are listed below.

- Use only proper cleaning solutions and devices. Using improper chemicals can degrade product quality and/or corrode your equipment. Using incorrect cleaning tools can scratch or damage dies or fixtures.

- Eliminate unacceptable equipment vibration. Excessive vibration can be an indicator of bearing failure or loose mounts or bolts.

- Identify any worn or broken components. Equipment operators can often easily recognize worn tooling, broken gauges, nonfunctioning sensors, and loose drive belts. Replacing such failing components improves your company's OEE.

- Eliminate all sources of contamination. Foreign materials, such as dust and foodstuffs, can quickly wear out your equipment. Preventing contamination helps to prolong equipment life.

Before you begin your autonomous maintenance activities, ask the following questions:

1. Is our equipment's performance, availability, or product quality significantly affected by one or more of the following?
   - Workplace contamination

- Lack of lubrication
- Loose bolts or screws

2. Is our workplace made unsafe by one or both of the following?
   - Workplace contamination
   - Fluid leaks

3. Are there any routine, "low-skill" maintenance procedures that our equipment operators can perform that would also serve one of the following purposes?
   - Enhance the operator's sense of ownership over the quality of the area and the work
   - Minimize machine downtime
   - Extend machine life

4. Do our equipment operators and maintenance personnel have a good working relationship? Will the implementation of autonomous maintenance strengthen that relationship?

   Tip Those times during which there are no pressing equipment problems or production deadlines are good opportunities for maintenance personnel to thoroughly review equipment with the operators. This helps build proactive, positive relationships among coworkers. For more ideas about building cooperation and teamwork, consult *The Team Memory Jogger*™.

Step 3: Create a planned maintenance program.

The term *planned maintenance* refers to maintenance activities that are performed on a set schedule. The goal of a preventive maintenance program is the elimination of the need for *reactive maintenance*, which is maintenance activities that are performed after a piece of equipment breaks.

The four stages of maintenance are listed below.

The Four Stages of Maintenance	
Maintenance Stage	**Description**
Reactive	Responding to breakdowns.
Preventive	Periodic checking, adjusting, and replacing of parts to prevent failures.
Predictive	Forecasting potential problems by measuring process variables and the condition of the equipment.
Maintenance prevention	Improving equipment design to eliminate the need for maintenance.

Your equipment's design determines most of its maintenance needs. Many companies work with their equipment suppliers to develop machines that require fewer and less-complicated maintenance procedures.

Design engineers can reduce the amount of required maintenance by placing an emphasis on maintainability, flexibility, and robustness. When maintenance tasks are simplified, then less skill, time, and effort are required to maintain the equipment.

TPM programs are most successful in companies that use a computerized maintenance management system (CMMS). Below are the basic elements of a CMMS.

1. A work-identification system that:
   - Specifies the problem (e.g., a needed repair on a piece of equipment).
   - Identifies where the problem is.
   - Assigns a priority to the problem.

2. A work-authorization system that:
   - Sorts all work requests.
   - Eliminates duplicate requests.

- Decides which work can be safely postponed.
- Turns approved repairs into work orders that are planned, scheduled, and executed.

3. A work management system for the maintenance department that:
   - Identifies the equipment or area that needs work.
   - Establishes communication with the person who requested the work.
   - Diagnoses the problem.
   - Orders the needed parts and materials.
   - Schedules a time for the repair to take place.

4. A preventive-maintenance system that:
   - Schedules and performs periodic checks on equipment, lubrication, and the replacement of worn parts.
   - Triggers work orders.
   - Tracks compliance with the production schedule.
   - Correlates preventive maintenance activities with equipment reliability and availability.

5. A system that records the entire performance and repair history of all critical machines.

6. A cost-reporting system that records all costs related to equipment maintenance, including hidden costs caused by the following factors:
   - Poor maintenance.
   - Downtime.
   - Defective products.
   - Lost opportunities.
   - Lost and dissatisfied customers.

Step 4: Establish an equipment life-cycle management program.

An equipment life-cycle management program maximizes the return on your company's equipment investment.

Such a program has five phases. These are outlined in the table below.

Equipment Life-Cycle Management Program	
Phase	**Description**
Specification	Identifies the functions and requirements of the equipment you intend to purchase.
Procurement	Matches your company's needs with a suitable external or internal equipment supplier.
Start-up or commissioning	The initial phase of the new equipment's operation. This phase lasts until the equipment reaches a stable state of operation.
Operation	Long-term supervision of the equipment. This includes production, maintenance, and rebuilding. The equipment generates value during its operation.
Disposal	Scrapping of all obsolete, deteriorating, or unneeded equipment.

> **Tip** Don't treat the five equipment life-cycle phases as separate categories; instead, integrate your company's efforts by working together in cross-functional teams.

> **Tip** To ensure that new equipment you purchase does the job for which it is intended, assemble a small team of design engineers, equipment suppliers, production engineers, shop-floor workers, and maintenance staff and have them

take part in the design and selection of the equipment, as well as the start-up process.

Tip Practice good equipment management principles to improve maintainability. For example, replace bearings that require ongoing lubrication with sealed bearings. Review data collected during maintenance activities to determine unsatisfactory equipment component lives. Then specify better components for all new equipment that you purchase.

Step 5: Plan for and conduct continuous-improvement activities.

Equipment operators and maintenance, engineering, and supervisory personnel should all take an active role in planning your company's continuous-improvement initiatives. These initiatives can include autonomous maintenance, planned preventive maintenance, and asset management (i.e., all activities and tasks performed throughout the asset life cycle). This focuses your entire company on responding to existing equipment needs as well as identifying new ones.

Once your continuous-improvement plans are in place for both your existing and new equipment needs, individuals and teams should conduct directed activities and report on their progress. These plans should be integrated into your company-wide lean initiatives and Total Quality Management (TQM) activities.

What does a typical TPM plan look like?

The stages of a typical TPM plan follow the Plan-Do-Check-Act (PDCA) Cycle, a powerful approach for problem solving. (See *The Problem Solving Memory Jogger*™ for details.) A sample plan is outlined in the table on the next page.

Sample TPM Plan

Plan

1. Assess your equipment's current condition to establish a baseline for future comparisons and performance standards. It's important to track the following data:
   - The percentage of "firefighting" that you must do.
   - Equipment failure rates.
   - Your maintenance budget as a percentage of asset-replacement value.
   - Your OEE rating.

2. Prepare to implement your TPM program by completing the following steps:
   - Inform all involved employees about it. Tell them what the program is, and what they will be expected to do.
   - Change your company's organizational structure, if necessary, to support and promote your TPM program.
   - Communicate your support of TPM to all employees and your improvement team.
   - Establish measurable goals and objectives.
   - Create a master implementation plan.

Do

3. Improve the effectiveness of each piece of your vital equipment by making sure the following steps are accomplished:
   - Operators learn about and begin to share in the basic care of their equipment (i.e., autonomous maintenance).
   - The maintenance department establishes a maintenance plan for all equipment.
   - Operators and maintenance staff are trained on maintenance procedures.
   - The maintenance department develops a total life-cycle maintenance program for your equipment.

Check

4. Check the effectiveness of your maintenance program by regularly examining your equipment's failure rate, downtime, defect rate, and OEE data.

Act

5. Recommend changes to your maintenance procedures and continue the improvement process.

6. Recommend new or modified equipment and parts standards to extend equipment life, improve serviceability, and reduce maintenance requirements.

Case example: Quick-Lite starts a TPM program

The team at Quick-Lite decides to start a TPM program for the company's computer networks, which have experienced a significant number of software and hardware failures. They begin by categorizing the various problems they are having with their systems, as described below.

Category 1: Availability. Quick-Lite's network goes down at least once a week for fifteen minutes, which affects nearly 250 people in jobs ranging from accounting to shipping. In addition, complaints logged into the IT service center indicate that nearly 85% of all the company's PCs experience some form of hardware or software failure. Most of these failures are overcome through rebooting the system.

The IT group estimates that roughly 150 hours per week of productive work time are lost to computer downtime. This equates to $7,500 in lost productivity costs per week—nearly $375,500 per year.

Category 2: Performance Efficiency. When the team at Quick-Lite takes a closer look at why employees' PCs must be rebooted, they find that having duel sessions of their Enterprise Resource Planning (ERP) system and local programs consumes a large quantity of memory. This either slows down the system or locks it up entirely. Keyboard failures are another problem.

Category 3: Quality. The team at Quick-Lite finds that data entry is the largest source of errors in the company's computer system.

After working hard to improve the company's network uptime, the team launches an autonomous maintenance program with the company's PC users.

This program consists of the following steps:

1. **Initial cleaning.**

   PC cleaning and inspection workshops are conducted within each work area. PC users are given the latest antivirus software and a software cleanup tool. During the initial cleaning activities, a physical inventory of both hardware and software is taken.

2. **Preventive cleaning measures.**

   The Quick-Lite team finds that certain work areas, such as insulator manufacturing, have high concentrations of ceramic dust. After cleaning the keyboards, the team installs soft plastic keyboard covers. Team members also set up a preventive maintenance schedule to clean out contamination within the computers' CPUs regularly.

3. **Development of cleaning standards.**

   Based on the results of their initial- and preventive-cleaning measures, the team at Quick-Lite decides to purchase an additional module for the IT group's customer-service software. This module allows them not only to schedule maintenance activities but also to allocate labor, materials, and equipment costs to assets. This enables the IT group to ensure that routine maintenance, upgrades, equipment replacements, and system purges are conducted. Job plans and safety instructions are developed for routine computer maintenance and repair activities.

4. **General inspection.**

   The team posts computer inspection guidelines within each work area, e-mails them to each user, and loads a reminder onto each PC. These guidelines include a schedule of the maintenance tasks to be done by IT personnel and PC operators.

5. **Autonomous inspections.**

   With the new cleaning tools and software in hand, each PC operator at Quick-Lite can now perform routine maintenance tasks. The IT group programs the cleaning software to conduct routine purges and defragmentation during a designated time established by each employee. A special internal web site is created to answer employees' most frequently asked questions about computer problems.

6. **Process discipline.**

   The team at Quick-Lite develops metrics to enable each work area to monitor its computer performance. This metric becomes the basis for a recognition system for the team that does the best job of improving the company's computer OEE.

7. **Independent autonomous maintenance.**

   Each department appoints at least one "power user," an employee who receives additional training about PC diagnostics and maintenance. This power user runs a weekly feedback and problem-solving meeting about the computer problems the department encountered during the previous week.

8. **Quick-Lite's computer problems soon begin to disappear.**

   Weekly maintenance activities are performed as expected, and Quick-Lite's PC operators are now able to conduct more difficult diagnostics on their own. Each department's weekly problem-solving meeting becomes a monthly, and then a quarterly, event.

Chapter 11
Lean Metrics

What are they?

Lean metrics are measurements that help you monitor your organization's progress toward achieving the goals of your lean initiative. Metrics fall into three categories: financial, behavioral, and core-process.

What do they do?

Lean metrics help employees understand how well your company is performing. They also encourage performance improvement by focusing employees' attention and efforts on your organization's lean goals.

Why use them?

Lean metrics enable you to measure, evaluate, and respond to your organization's current performance in a balanced way—without sacrificing the quality of your products or services to meet quantity objectives or increasing your product inventory levels to raise machine efficiency. Properly designed lean metrics also enable you to consider the important people factors necessary for your organization's success.

What are the objectives of using lean metrics?

1. After you use lean metrics to verify that you are successfully meeting your company's lean goals, you can do the following:

   a. Use the data you have collected to determine existing problems. Then you can evaluate and

---

prioritize any issues that arise based on your findings.

    b. Identify improvement opportunities and develop action plans for them.

    c. Develop objectives for performance goals that you can measure (e.g., 100% first-time-through quality capability = zero defects made or passed on to downstream processes).

    d. Evaluate the progress you have made toward meeting your company's performance goals.

2. Lean metrics help you analyze your business more accurately in the following areas:

    a. Determining critical business issues, such as high inventory levels that drive up operational costs, poor quality levels that create customer dissatisfaction, and extended lead times that cause late deliveries and lost orders.

    b. Determining whether you are adhering to lean metrics. These differ from traditional metrics, which can actually work against you. For example, adhering to traditional metrics such as machine efficiency can spur over-production, and improving your inventory turnover can worsen your on-time-delivery performance.

    c. Determining the best way to use your organization's resources. For example, you can ask questions such as "What is our most frequent problem?" and "What is our costliest problem?"

How can I be sure I am collecting the right type of data?

Before your team begins to collect data, ask the following questions:

1. What is our purpose for collecting this data?

2. Will the data tell us what we need to know?

3. Will we be able to act on the data we collect?

Your goal is to create an easy-to-use, high-impact measurement system.

An easy-to-use system must require minimal human involvement. The higher the level of human involvement required, the lower the accuracy of the data and the more time needed for data collection. Try to find ways to automate your data collection and charting.

A high-impact measurement system is one that results in information that is useful and easily interpreted.

> **Tip** Use a standard definition form for your metrics. The form should answer the following questions:
>
> - What type of metric is it (financial, behavioral, or core-process)?
> - Why was it selected?
> - Where will the data be obtained?
> - How will the data be collected?
> - What formula will be used for calculating the metric?
> - How often will it be calculated?
> - How often will the metric be used?

Revise your definition form as needed.

Tip Use basic graphs (e.g., line, bar, and pie graphs) and statistical process control (SPC) charts to display your data. These charts give you insight into data trends, reveal whether true process changes have occurred, and show if the process is capable of achieving your desired performance objectives. Other data-analysis techniques might be required to conduct effective problem solving. (See chapter 5, "Error Proofing," for details.)

How do I design a data-collection process?

When you design your data-collection process, keep the following points in mind:

- Make sure that all employees who will collect the data are involved in the design of your data-collection process.

- Tell employees that the main driver for data collection is process improvement, not finger-pointing.

- Tell all involved employees how the data will be used.

- Design data-collection forms to be user-friendly.

- When developing a data-collection procedure, describe how much data is to be collected, when the data is to be collected, who will collect the data, and how the data is to be recorded.

- Automate data collection and charting whenever possible.

- Involve employees in the interpretation of the data.

Tip Avoid the following pitfalls:

- Measuring everything. Focus instead on the few critical measures that can verify performance levels and guide your improvement efforts.

- Misinterpreting data. Show employees why and how the data was captured. Also tell how the data will be used in your lean enterprise initiative.

- Collecting unused data. Data collection is time consuming. Ensure that all the data you collect will be put to good use.

- Communicating performance data inappropriately. Avoid creating harmful fault-finding, public humiliation, or overzealous competition.

Tip Remember to use the appropriate tools for your analysis. Less-experienced teams can use basic tools such as Pareto Charts, Histograms, Run Charts, Scatter Diagrams, and Control Charts. Refer to *The Memory Jogger™ II* for insight on the purpose and use of these tools. More-expert teams can use advanced tools such as regression analysis, design of experiments, and analysis of variance (ANOVA).

Tip Most metrics reveal ranges of values and averages of multiple measures. However, your customers rarely experience an "average." Each opportunity for a defect is an opportunity for failure in your customers' eyes.

Tip As you work toward improvement, you might find that solving the smallest problems takes up most of your time. You might spend 80% of your improvement efforts fixing 20% of the things that go wrong.

What are financial metrics, and how do I implement them?

You improve your organization's financial performance by lowering the total cost of operations and increasing revenue. If your company can become a lower-cost producer without sacrificing quality, service, or product performance, it can strengthen its performance and market position.

Examples of Financial Metrics
Costs
• Cash flow
• Direct and indirect labor costs
• Direct and indirect materials costs
• Facility and operational costs
• Production systems
• Information systems
• Inventory-carrying costs
• Total cost of ownership
Revenue
• Sales
• Gross margins
• Earnings before interest and taxes
• Return on assets
• Return on investment
• Warranty costs
• Product profitability

When making revenue or savings projections, it's important to understand the difference between hard- and soft-cost savings. *Hard-cost savings* actually produce cash savings or profit increases. They directly affect your company's profit-and-loss statement.

Soft-cost savings are assets that are freed up so they can be used for another purpose. This contributes no positive change to a company's P&L statement.

It's also important to avoid _cost shifting_, which is the act of moving costs from one account to another without creating any real savings. Cost shifting often hides waste rather than removing it. Your ultimate goal is to reduce both your hard- and soft-cost savings for the benefit of the whole organization.

Case example: Quick-Lite implements a quick-changeover initiative

Quick-Lite is a hypothetical company that manufactures spark plugs. Its improvement team decides to implement a quick-changeover initiative for the company's shell-fabrication line. This enables Quick-Lite to reduce its batch sizes by a full 65% and its inventory investment by 35%. These are both hard-cost savings.

Before Quick-Lite implemented its cost-reduction efforts, employees were responsible for all aspects of inventory and stocking. Now Quick-Lite requires one of its suppliers to inventory and stock all raw materials at its own site. By doing this, Quick-Lite frees up nearly 50% of its storage space, for which it has no plans for other uses. This is a soft-cost savings.

By requiring one of its suppliers to inventory and stock raw materials at its own site, Quick-Lite has shifted the cost of stocking the raw material to its supplier. However, the supplier might now decide to pass this expense back to Quick-Lite in the form of higher prices, which Quick-Lite might have to pass along to its customers.

> **Tip** Introduce financial metrics to employees as a way for them to understand the impact of their lean efforts on operations as well as on the company's bottom line.

> **Tip** Encourage the use of financial metrics in your team-based improvement activities. Provide training when necessary.

What are behavioral metrics, and how do I implement them?

Behavioral metrics are measurements that help you monitor the actions and attitudes of your employees.

Employees' commitment, communication, and cooperation all have a significant impact on your organization's success. Financial and core-process metrics alone cannot show whether employees are working together in a cooperative spirit. Your company's long-term success is possible only when employees' behavior is aligned and everyone works for the benefit of the entire organization.

Behavioral Categories and Metrics
Category: Commitment
Performance Metrics
<ul><li>Adherence to policies and procedures</li><li>Participation levels in lean improvement activities</li><li>Availability and dedication of human-resources department</li><li>Efforts to train employees as needed</li></ul>
Category: Communication
Performance Metrics
<ul><li>Customer/employee surveys regarding quantity and quality of company communications efforts</li><li>Elimination of service or production errors caused by ineffective communications</li><li>Error-reporting accuracy and timeliness</li><li>Formal recognition of employees' communication efforts</li></ul>
Category: Cooperation
Performance Metrics
<ul><li>Shared financial risks and rewards</li><li>Effective efforts toward reporting and resolving problems</li><li>Joint recognition activities</li><li>Formal recognition of employees' cooperation efforts</li></ul>

Tip Customer and employee satisfaction surveys and core-process metrics measure behavioral performance only indirectly. More effective and direct ways to measure it include project feedback, meeting evaluations, employee appraisals, and peer evaluations.

Tip Conduct teamwork and facilitation training to improve cooperation and communication within your organization. See *The Team Memory Jogger*™ and *Facilitation at a Glance!*™ for details.

Tip Make sure your reward-and-recognition system is aligned with your company's lean goals. See *Performance Management: A Pocket Guide for Employee Development*™ for details.

What are core-process metrics, and how do I implement them?

There are many different types of core-process metrics, which allow you to measure the performance of your core processes (see Glossary) in different ways.

Be sure to measure all your core processes for both productivity and results. *Productivity, the ratio of output to input, provides data about the efficiency of your core processes.* Tracking the results and then comparing them to your desired outcomes provides you with information about their effectiveness. Some general core-process metrics are shown in the table below.

Core-Process Metrics
• New product launches
• New product extensions
• Product failures
• Design-cycle time
• Time to market
• Product life-cycle profitability

Product life-cycle metrics include the identification of market potential, product design, new product launches, model extensions, product use, and product obsolescence.

Order-fulfillment-cycle metrics include activities related to sales, engineering, procurement, production planning and scheduling, the production process, inventory management, warehousing, shipping, and invoicing.

Some specific core-process metrics are shown in the table below. These metrics are explained in detail on the following pages.

Core-Process Metrics	
Results Metrics	**Productivity Metrics**
• Health and safety (HS) • First-time-through (FTT) quality • Rolled-throughput yield (RTY) • On-time delivery (OTD) • Dock-to-dock (DTD) • Order-fulfillment lead time (OFLT)	• Inventory turnover (ITO) rate • Build to schedule (BTS) • Overall equipment effectiveness (OEE) • Value-added to non-value-added (VA/NVA) ratio

What are health and safety metrics?

Health and safety (HS) metrics measure the impact of your production processes on employees' health and safety.

Why use them?

A wholesome and safe workplace improves the availability and performance of your organization's human resources. Operations costs improve when insurance rates are lowered, the cost of replacing workers is reduced, and production assets are more available. In addition, improved morale and a sense of well-being increase employee productivity and participation in your company's improvement initiatives.

HS conditions can be measured in several ways. Metrics to consider when evaluating HS include days lost due to accidents, absenteeism, employee turnover, and experience modification ratio (EMR), a method used by insurance companies to set rates. (A detailed explanation of EMR is beyond the scope of this book.)

What is first time through (FTT)? LEADER

First time through (FTT) is a metric that measures the percentage of units that go through your production process without being scrapped, rerun, retested, returned by the downstream operation, or diverted into an off-line repair area. This metric is also applicable to processes related to services your company provides. For example, you can use it to measure the number of sales orders processed without error the first time they go through your work processes.

Why use it?

- Increased process/output quality reduces the need for excess production inventory, improving your dock-to-dock (DTD) time. (See page 138 for a definition of DTD.)

- It improves your ability to maintain proper sequence throughout the process, improving the build-to-schedule (BTS) metric. (See page 143 for a definition of BTS.)

- Increasing quality before the constraint operation (see Glossary) occurs ensures that that operation receives no defective parts. This enables you to increase your quality rate and reduce defects at the constraint operation. This in turn improves the overall-equipment-effectiveness (OEE) metric. (See page 147 for a definition of OEE.)

- Your organization's total cost is improved due to lower warranty, scrap, and repair costs.

FTT is calculated using the following formula. (Remember that "units" can be finished products, components, or sales orders; FTT's use is not limited to a production environment.)

$$FTT = \frac{\text{units entering process} - (\text{scrap} + \text{reruns} + \text{retests} + \text{repaired off-line} + \text{returns})}{\text{units entering process}}$$

Case example: Quick-Lite calculates its FTT

At Quick-Lite's spark-plug-shell machining center, 250,500 shells are produced during an eight-hour shift. Of these, 4,450 are scrapped; none are rerun, retested, or repaired; and 4,318 are returned by the downstream operation. This equals an FTT of 96.5%, as shown below.

$$FTT = \frac{250,500 - (4,450 + 0 + 4,318)}{250,500} = 0.965, \text{ or } 96.5\%$$

Quick-Lite can easily calculate the total FTT capabilities of its four operations involved in spark-plug-shell fabrication by multiplying the FTT results for each operation. These results are as follows: cut bar stock, 95%; machine shell, 96.5%; thread shell, 97%; and weld side wire, 98%.

With this data, Quick-Lite calculated its overall FTT as follows:

$$FTT = 95\% \times 96.5\% \times 97\% \times 98\% = 87\%$$

What is rolled throughput yield (RTY)?

Rolled throughput yield (RTY) is a metric that measures the probability that a process will be completed without a defect occurring. Six Sigma programs use this metric either instead of or in parallel with FTT.

RTY is based on the number of defects per opportunity (DPO). An *opportunity* is anything you measure, test, or inspect. It can be a part, product, or service characteristic that is critical to customer-quality expectations or requirements.

How does RTY differ from FTT?

FTT measures how well you create units of product; RTY measures how well you create quality. While FTT measures at the unit level and finds the percentage of defective parts, RTY measures at the defect level and finds how many defects a particular part has.

The RTY metric is sensitive to product complexity, as well as the number of opportunities for defects present in a production process or aspect of a service. RTY can help you focus an investigation when you narrow down a problem within a complex or multi-step process.

To calculate RTY, you must first calculate defects per unit (DPU) and defects per opportunity (DPO). The result is then used to calculate RTY.

$$DPU = \frac{\text{number of defects per unit}}{\text{total number of units}}$$

Defects per opportunity (DPO) is the probability of a defect occurring in any one product, service characteristic, or process step. It is calculated as follows:

$$DPO = \frac{DPU}{\text{opportunities per unit}}$$

Finally, RTY is calculated as follows:

$$RTY = 1 - DPO$$

Case example: Quick-Lite calculates its RTY

Quick-Lite has four operations involved in its spark-plug-shell fabrication process. Each operation has five opportunities and a DPO of 0.001. The RTY is calculated as follows:

$$1 - 0.001 = 0.999$$

$$RTY = (.999^5)^4 = (.995)^4 = 0.98$$

What is on-time delivery (OTD)?

On-time delivery (OTD) is a metric that measures the percentage of units you produce that meet your customer's deadline. For this metric, a unit is defined as a line item on a sales order or delivery ticket.

Why use it?

- OTD provides a holistic measurement of whether you have met your customer's expectations for having the right product, at the right place, at the right time.

- You can use OTD to track deliveries at both the line-item and order levels. OTD alerts you to internal process issues at the line-item level and shows their effect on your customers at the order level.

- OTD ensures that you are meeting optimum customer-service levels. When you balance OTD with the other internally focused core-process metrics—build-to-schedule (BTS), inventory turnover (ITO) rate, and dock-to-dock (DTD)—you can meet your customer-service goals without making an excessive inventory investment.

©2002 GOAL/QPC

OTD is calculated on an order-by-order basis at the line-item level using the following formula:

$$OTD = \frac{\text{line items received on time by the customer}}{\text{total line items received}}$$

Tip Sometimes OTD is measured at the order level rather than at the line-item level. When this is the case, the entire order is considered to be late if only one line item is late. Be sure to verify the level at which your customer wants OTD measured.

Case example: Quick-Lite calculates its OTD

Quick-Lite ships an order with six line items on it. One of these items is delivered late. If Quick-Lite tracks the OTD at the order level, then the total order is late, or 0% on time.

Last month, Quick-Lite shipped a total of 1,250 line items, of which 1,115 were delivered on time. Therefore, the monthly on-time delivery performance is 89.2%, as shown below.

$$OTD = \frac{1,115}{1,250} = .892, \text{ or } 89.2\%$$

Tip If delivery occurs on the same day as the ship day, then you can use line items shipped on time to measure your OTD.

Tip In the case of delivery windows (i.e., specified time frames for deliveries), early deliveries might not be considered to be on time.

Tip Only the customer can choose to change the required delivery time.

Tip Track customer request dates as well as internal ship/promise dates whenever these two dates are not the same.

What is dock-to-dock (DTD)?

Dock-to-dock (DTD) is a metric that measures how long it takes raw materials or sub-components coming into your plant to be turned into finished products.

Why use it?

- Improving your DTD time improves your company's ability to make on-time deliveries.

- Improving your DTD time lowers your materials-handling, obsolescence, and inventory-carrying costs, which in turn leads to a lower total cost.

- Having decreased inventory levels leads to less storage and handling of materials. Thus, fewer opportunities to damage parts arise, and your FTT is improved.

DTD is calculated using the following formula:

$$DTD = \frac{\text{total number of control parts}}{\text{end-of-line rate}}$$

A *control part* is a significant component of the final product that travels through all the major manufacturing processes for that product.

The *end-of-line rate* is the average number of jobs per hour for a particular product. It is calculated using the following formula:

$$\text{end-of-line rate} = \frac{\text{manufactured units/week}}{\text{production hours/week}}$$

Case example: Quick-Lite calculates its DTD

Quick-Lite designated its R56T spark-plug shell as the control part. This shell goes through five distinct manufacturing processes before it is ready for shipment to the customer. Quick-Lite calculated its weekly DTD as follows:

$$\text{end-of-line rate} = \frac{43,440 \text{ units}}{48 \text{ hours}} = 905 \text{ units per hour}$$

Quick-Lite's current inventory of R56T spark-plug shells is as follows:

Current Inventory	
Inventory Locations	**Units in Area**
Raw Materials	53,000
Cut	2,345
Machine	1,205
Thread	1,195
Weld	1,098
Assembly	14,480
Finished Goods	73,005
Total	146,328

$$\text{DTD} = \frac{\text{total units}}{\text{end-of-line rate}}$$

$$\text{DTD} = \frac{146,328 \text{ units}}{905 \text{ units/hour}} = 161.7 \text{ hours}$$

Quick-Lite also calculated its total DTD because it manufactures the control part during only six eight-hour shifts per week. The number of hours it would take to process all the units on hand in six eight-hour shifts per week is calculated as follows:

$$\text{Total DTD} = \text{DTD} \times \frac{\text{total hours/week}}{\text{production hours/week}}$$

$$\text{Total DTD} = 161.7 \text{ hours} \times \frac{168 \text{ hours}}{48 \text{ hours}} = 565.9 \text{ hours}$$

These calculations show that Quick-Lite, with nearly seventy-one days' worth of production in inventory, is like many other companies that make the mistake of purchasing large quantities of raw materials, running large batches, and overproducing.

> **Tip** Organizations often mistakenly compare their DTD measurement with their OTD. However, OTD does not measure invoice time; it stops at the point of shipment. By improving your DTD, you will automatically improve your OTD.

What is order-fulfillment lead time (OFLT)?

Order-fulfillment lead time (OFLT) is the average time that elapses between your company's receipt of an order from a customer and when you send an invoice to your customer for the finished product or service. It extends the DTD metric to include all your sales order-entry, sales-engineering, production-planning, and procurement lead times before production, as well as your invoicing lead times after production.

Why use it?

The time from receipt of a sales order to the time of receipt of payment is a measure of your company's operating cash flow. This is the money that your company uses to invest in its human resources, materials, equipment, and facilities. How your company manages its cash flow affects the company's ability to acquire investors and borrow the money it needs to expand its business.

Case example: Quick-Lite calculates its OFLT

Quick-Lite developed its OFLT calculation based on the average time the company took to perform

---

the following separate operations. (The team decided to exclude receipt of payment from their calculations.)

- Sales order (SO): The time from when an order is received until the time it is entered into the production-scheduling system.

- Production scheduling (PS): The time from when an order enters the production-scheduling system until the time actual production begins.

- Manufacturing (M): The time from when a manufacturing order is started until the order is released to the shipping department.

- Shipping (S): The time from when an order is received in the shipping department until it leaves the dock.

- Invoice (I): The time from when accounting is notified of a shipment going out until it sends the invoice to the customer.

Thus, OFLT = SO + PS + M + S + I.

For Quick-Lite, OFLT = 1 + 2 + 5 + 2 + 2 = 12 days.

> ***Tip*** Some companies break down their OFLT into separate financial measures, such as sales days outstanding (i.e., the average number of equivalent sales days currently out in receivables). This breakdown is often called quote-to-cash cycle time.

> ***Tip*** To focus your team's efforts, consider breaking down the OFLT into discrete measures within each functional area (e.g., sales, engineering, scheduling, procurement, and accounting), as shown in the Quick-Lite example above. Have each functional area develop value stream maps and then focus its improvement efforts on waste elimination and lead-time reduction.

What is inventory turnover (ITO) rate?

Inventory turnover (ITO) rate is a metric that measures how fast your company sells the products you make—that is, how efficient your marketing efforts are.

Why use it?

- Inventory costs are a significant portion of your company's total logistics-related costs.

- Your inventory levels affect your customer-service levels, especially if a customer's order lead time is less than your manufacturing lead time.

- Your company's decisions regarding service levels and inventory levels have a significant effect on how much of the company's money is tied up in inventory investment. This is commonly referred to as "inventory carrying cost."

- High ITO rates reduce your risk of inventory loss and keep your return-on-assets rates competitively high.

- A low ITO rate can indicate excess inventory or poor sales—both bad signs. A high ITO rate, on the other hand, can indicate high efficiency.

Most companies struggle with low, single-digit ITO rates. The goal of most lean organizations is to achieve at least a double-digit ITO rate. A few exceptional companies are able to achieve triple-digit ITO rates across all their product lines.

ITO is calculated using the following formula:

$$\text{ITO} = \frac{\text{cost of goods sold (COGS)}}{\text{year-end inventory (taken from your company's balance sheet)}}$$

Case example: Quick-Lite calculates its ITO

The people at Quick-Lite thought they were only in the spark-plug business. What they didn't realize, until they did the calculations below, was that they were also in the spark-plug *inventory* business.

$$ITO = \frac{\$275,000,000}{\$63,953,500} = 4.3 \text{ turns}$$

Tip Some companies calculate their ITO rates based on measurements other than COGS. Some use yearly sales. Raw-materials producers often use the average purchase price for raw materials. Other companies estimate the average value of the work-in-progress (WIP) components at each production step.

What is build to schedule (BTS)?

Build to schedule (BTS) is a metric that measures the percentage of units scheduled for production on a given day that are actually produced on the correct day, in the correct mix, and in the correct sequence.

Why use it?

- BTS measures your company's ability to produce what your customers want, when they want it, and in the scheduled production order.

- BTS alerts you to potential overproduction situations.

- BTS enables you to lower your inventory levels and improve your DTD time.

- The lower materials-handling and inventory-carrying costs that should result when you use BTS lead to improved total cost results for your company.

BTS is calculated using the following formula:

$$\text{BTS} = \frac{\text{volume performance} \times \text{mix performance}}{\times \text{sequence performance}}$$

The calculation for determining volume performance is as follows:

$$\text{volume performance} = \frac{\text{actual number of units produced}}{\text{scheduled number of units}}$$

where "actual number of units produced" is the number of units of a given product to come off the end of the line on a given day, and "scheduled number of units" is the number of units of a given product scheduled to be produced. The result of the calculation is a percentage.

The calculation for determining mix performance is as follows:

$$\text{mix performance} = \frac{\text{actual number of units built to mix}}{\substack{\text{actual units produced or} \\ \text{units scheduled to be produced}}}$$

where "actual number of units built to mix" is the number of units built that are included in the daily production schedule (i.e., no overbuilds are counted). You can use either the number of actual units produced or the number of units scheduled to be produced, whichever is lower.

The calculation for determining sequence performance is as follows:

$$\text{sequence performance} = \frac{\substack{\text{actual number of} \\ \text{units built to schedule}}}{\text{actual units built to mix}}$$

where "actual number of units built to schedule" equals the number of units built on a given day in the scheduled order.

Case example: Quick-Lite calculates its BTS performance

Quick-Lite was painfully aware of its schedule mix-ups, overproduction, and inability to consistently match its production schedules to the ship dates that had been promised to its customers. The company decided to use BTS as a measure to ensure compliance to the scheduling and production requirements. What follows is a description of how Quick-Lite calculated its BTS performance.

The company had scheduled three types of spark plugs for one day's production. The table below shows the three spark-plug types and their build sequences:

Spark-Plug Types and Build Sequences		
Spark-Plug Type	**Build Sequence**	**Assemblies Scheduled**
R56T	1	7,240
45TS	2	12,500
37CTS	3	3,450
Total		23,190
Spark-Plug Type	**Actual Sequence**	**Assemblies Built**
R56T	1	6,250
37CTS	2	3,375
45TS	3	13,900
Total		23,525

$$\text{Volume} = \frac{23,525}{23,190} = 1.01, \text{ or } 100\%*$$

*No credit is given for overproduction.

Using the formula shown on the previous page, Quick-Lite calculated its mix performance as follows:

Mix Performance	
Spark-Plug Type	Assemblies Built to Mix
R56T	6,250
37CTS	3,375
45TS	12,500
Total	22,125

$$\text{Mix} = \frac{22,125}{23,190} = 0.954, \text{ or } 95.4\%$$

Quick-Lite's sequence performance is as follows:

Sequence Performance			
Spark-Plug Type	Scheduled Sequence	Actual Sequence	Assemblies Built to Sequence
R56T	1	1	6,250
37CTS	3	2	3,375
45TS	2	3	0 (37CTS built before 45TS)
Total			9,625

$$\text{Sequence} = \frac{9,625}{22,125} = 0.435, \text{ or } 43.5\%$$

This day's performance, then, was as follows:

$$\text{BTS} = 100\% \times 95.4\% \times 43.5\% = 41.5\%$$

Thus, Quick-Lite succeeded in making its volume goal; however, it did not produce the correct quantities in the correct sequence. Instead, it overproduced—and, because of schedule mix-ups, it missed customer-delivery windows.

What is overall equipment effectiveness (OEE)?

Overall equipment effectiveness (OEE) is a metric that measures the availability, performance efficiency, and quality rate of your equipment. It is especially important to calculate OEE for your constraint operation.

Why use it?

- A higher throughput rate reduces the time your equipment spends in process, thereby decreasing your total DTD time.

- More stable processes improve your production predictability, thereby improving your BTS.

- Higher throughput and lower rework and scrap costs lead to improved total costs.

OEE is calculated using the following formula:

$$OEE = \frac{equipment\ availability \times performance\ efficiency \times quality}{}$$

The calculation for determining equipment availability is as follows:

$$Equipment\ availability = \frac{operating\ time}{net\ available\ time}$$

"Operating time" is the net available time minus all other downtime (i.e., breakdowns, setup time, and maintenance). "Net available time" is the total scheduled time minus contractually required downtime (i.e., paid lunches and breaks).

Case example: Quick-Lite calculates its OEE performance

Quick-Lite calculated its spark-plug-shell machining center's equipment availability as follows:

Equipment Availability	
Machine #5127	**Calendar Week: 35**
A. Total scheduled time	6,000 minutes
B. Required downtime	500 minutes
C. Net available time (A–B)	5,500 minutes
D. Other downtime	850 minutes
E. Operating time (C–D)	4,650 minutes

$$\text{Equipment availability} = \frac{4,650 \text{ minutes}}{5,500 \text{ minutes}} = 0.845, \text{ or } 84.5\%$$

The calculation for determining performance efficiency is as follows:

$$\text{performance efficiency} = \frac{\text{total parts run} \times \text{ideal cycle time}}{\text{operating time}}$$

where "total parts run" equals the total number of parts produced (regardless of quality), and "ideal cycle time" equals the greatest of the following: the normal expected cycle time (in seconds per part) for the equipment; the best cycle time ever achieved and sustained for that piece of equipment; and an estimate based on experience with similar equipment.

Quick-Lite calculated the performance efficiency of its spark-plug-shell machining center as follows:

$$\text{performance efficiency} = \frac{0.0167 \text{ minutes} \times 250,500}{4,650} = 0.898, \text{ or } 89.8\%$$

The calculation for determining quality is as follows:

$$\text{quality} = \frac{\text{total parts run} - \text{total defects}}{\text{total parts run}}$$

where "total defects" equals the number of rejected, reworked, or scrapped parts.

This is identical to the FTT calculation shown on page 134. Quick-Lite calculated the quality of its spark-plug-shell machining center as follows:

$$\text{quality} = \frac{250,500 - (4{,}450 + 0 + 4{,}318)}{250{,}500} = 0.965, \text{ or } 96.5\%$$

Quick-Lite then calculated the OEE performance for its spark-plug-shell machining center as follows:

$$\text{OEE} = 84.5\% \times 89.8\% \times 96.5\% = 73.2\%$$

Tip Do not compare OEE results for non-identical machines or processes. An OEE comparison should be done only at time intervals for the same machine or the same process; otherwise, it is meaningless.

What is the VA/NVA ratio? LEADER

The value-added to non-value-added (VA/NVA) ratio is a metric that compares the amount of time in your work process spent on value-added activities to the amount of time spent on non-value-added activities.

Why use it?

- It makes non-value-added activities evident.
- It focuses your lean improvement efforts on the elimination of waste and the reduction of lead time.
- It provides a common metric for your management, sales, engineering, production, and procurement departments to communicate their priorities to each other and conduct cross-functional improvement activities.

VA/NVA ratio is calculated using the following formula:

$$\text{VA/NVA} = \frac{\text{total value-added activities time}}{\text{total OFLT}}$$

Case example: Quick-Lite calculates its VA/NVA ratio

To determine their total value-added activities time, the team at Quick-Lite developed a value stream map of their order-fulfillment process. They observed or calculated times for each activity. From this map they were able to identify the value-added and non-value-added activities.

From these results, the Quick-Lite team considered only their order-entry and manufacturing activities as value-added. Because all other activities were necessary but did not add value to the product, they were considered to be non-value-added activities.

Quick-Lite's weekly production hours included three daily shifts for five days, for a total of twenty hours per day (100 hours per week). The team at Quick-Lite calculated their VA/NVA performance as follows. (See the section on OFLT for details on the meaning of the letters used in the equation below.)

$$VA = SO + PS + M + S + I$$

$$VA = 10 + 0 + 235 + 0 + 0 = 245 \text{ minutes}$$

Recall that the Quick-Lite team calculated their OFLT as follows:

$$OFLT = SO + PS + M + S + I$$

$$OFLT = 1 + 2 + 5 + 2 + 2 = 12 \text{ days}$$

$$VA/NVA =$$

$$\frac{245 \text{ minutes}/60 \text{ minutes per hour}}{\begin{array}{c} 8 \text{ hours} + 16 \text{ hours} + 100 \text{ hours} \\ + 16 \text{ hours} + 16 \text{ hours} \end{array}} = 0.026 \text{ , or } 2.6\%$$

The result of 2.6% was an eye-opener for the team at Quick-Lite. They conducted a benchmarking study and found that most companies that perform this calculation do so for their manufacturing processes only. Their manufacturing-only VA/NVA percentages ranged from about 15% to 35%. However, adding their sales, production-planning, shipping, and invoicing times significantly reduced their VA/NVA ratio.

> **Tip** To focus your efforts, consider breaking the VA/NVA ratio into discrete measures within each functional area of your company (e.g., sales, engineering, scheduling, procurement, and accounting). Have each functional area develop value stream maps (see chapter 3 for details) and focus its improvement efforts on waste elimination and lead-time reduction.

How do I decide what performance metrics to use? LEADER

Your goal is to select the metrics that accurately portray your company's performance. The best approach is to balance the metrics you use among the three categories (financial, behavioral, and core-process) and to use a mix of in-process and end-of-process metrics.

You should also consider the total number of metrics you use. Using too many can confuse employees and slow your performance-improvement efforts. Using too few might not provide you with enough detail to properly focus your improvement efforts.

When deciding which metrics to use, consider the following points:

- What are you measuring?
- What will be the frequency of measurement?
- How long will data be collected?
- Who will measure it?
- How will it be measured?
- How will it be charted?
- What action will be taken after the data is interpreted?
- Who will be responsible for follow-up action?

An Example of
a Balanced Measurement Selection

Category: Financial				
Measure-ment	Freq.	Who Measures?	How Measured?	How Charted?
Cost reductions	Monthly	Improve-ment teams	Hard- and soft-cost transactional cost analysis	Bar chart indicating monthly and cumulative totals by location
Cost increases	Monthly	Improve-ment teams	Hard- and soft-cost transactional cost analysis	Bar chart indicating monthly and cumulative totals by location
Category: Behavioral				
Customer satisfac-tion	Yearly	Quality department	Customer survey— questions weighted by satisfaction and importance	Bar chart
Employee satisfac-tion	Yearly	Steering team	Employee survey— questions weighted by satisfaction and importance	Bar chart
Lean improve-ment initiative comple-tions	Monthly	Improve-ment teams	Number of lean improvement initiatives completed with desired results	Bar chart indicating monthly and cumulative totals by location

Category: Core-Process				
Measure-ment	Freq.	Who Measures?	How Measured?	How Charted?
On-time delivery	Monthly	Sales and manufac-turing	OTD % at line-item level, by ship-to locations	Pareto Chart
BTS	Monthly	Production planning	Volume × mix × sequence	Chart of individuals and moving range
OEE	Monthly	Manufac-turing	Availability × performance efficiency × FTT quality for constraining operation and lowest-availability assets	Chart of individuals and moving range
ITO rate	Monthly	Finance	Inventory turns (cost of goods sold ÷ average inventory value)	Chart of individuals and moving range
OFLT	Monthly	Aggregated by functions submitted to lean enterprise	Average OFLT by product family	Chart of individuals and moving range

Tip As you complete your measurement selection, set specific performance objectives to drive your evaluation and improvement efforts.

What is a lean enterprise scorecard?   LEADER

A lean enterprise scorecard is a technique for comparing your actual results to your performance objectives.

Below is Quick-Lite's scorecard. It shows how the company used scoring to gauge its overall progress toward its goals. (See Scoring Guide on page 156.)

Monthly Performance by Site: May		Site A		Site B		Site C	
Category	Goal	Actual	Score	Actual	Score	Actual	Score
1. Monthly cost reductions (% of operating budget)	0.5%	0.45%	6	0.6%	10	0.4%	4
2. Percentage of products having undergone a lean transformation	12%	15%	10	10%	4	9%	2
3. Improvement suggestions	25	21	4	17	0	12	0
4. FTT quality	100%	92%	6	81%	4	78%	2
5. OTD (based on line items shipped)	98%	97% (of 128)	8	94% (of 124)	8	99% (of 198)	10
6. DTD	10 days	12	6	14	2	15	0
7. BTS	100%	75%	2	90%	6	85%	4
8. OEE for constraining operation	Per target: no less than 85%	Target = 95%	8	Target = 94%	4	Target = 93%	6
		89%		79%		88%	
9. ITO rate	5	4.6	6	4	4	3.9	2
10. OFLT	5 days	5 days	10	7 days	6	6 days	8
Totals (out of a possible 100 points)			66		48		38

Quick-Lite's Lean Scorecard for One Calendar Year

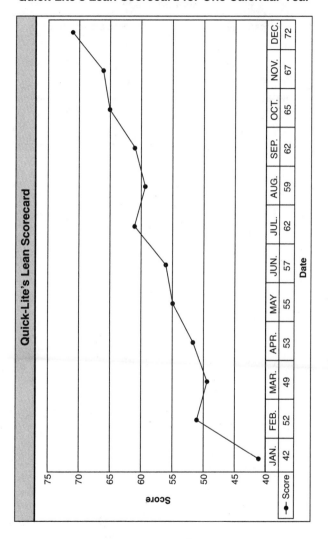

	JAN.	FEB.	MAR.	APR.	MAY	JUN.	JUL.	AUG.	SEP.	OCT.	NOV.	DEC.
Score	42	52	49	53	55	57	62	59	62	65	67	72

Scoring Guide	
Percentage of Goal	**Days to Complete Goal**
100%: 10 points	≤ 0 days: 10 points
95–98%: 8 points	+1 day: 8 points
90–94%: 6 points	+2 days: 6 points
80–89%: 4 points	+3 days: 4 points
70–79%: 2 points	+4 days: 2 points
<69%: 0 points	+5 days: 0 points

Glossary

Activity-Based Costing (ABC) An accounting technique that enables an organization to determine the actual cost of a product or service by tracing the cost back to the specific activities that produce or provide it. Compare to *Traditional Cost Accounting (TCA)*.

asymmetry When opposite sides of a part, tool, material, or fixture are different in size, shape, or relative position. Asymmetrical differences can be hard to spot, resulting in errors. Compare to *symmetry*.

autonomous maintenance A program in which equipment operators share responsibility with maintenance staff for the care of the equipment they use.

batch delay The amount of time a service operation or product unit waits while other operations or units in the lot, or batch, are completed or processed.

batch processing The movement of products through the manufacturing process in large numbers of identical units at once. Entire batches, or lots, are sent to each operation in the production process at the same time. Also known as *large-lot processing*. Compare to *one-piece flow*.

BTS (build to schedule) A metric that measures the percentage of units scheduled for production on a given day that are actually produced on the correct day, in the correct mix, and in the correct sequence.

capacity The ability of a machine and its operator to complete the work required.

constant order-cycle system An inventory-control system that features a fixed reorder date and a varying order quantity.

constant order-quantity system An inventory-control system that features a fixed order quantity and a varying reorder date.

constraining operation The manufacturing step that determines the upper limit on the number of finished parts that can be produced within a value stream. Also known as a *bottleneck operation*.

constraint operation An operation that is long in duration or is critical to completing a manufacturing process.

contact method An error-proofing method that involves inspecting the size, shape, or color of an object to determine if any deviations exist.

core processes The essential activities an organization must perform to produce products, complete order-fulfillment functions, maintain its assets, and complete all supporting business functions.

cost shifting Moving costs from one account to another without creating any real savings. Cost shifting often hides waste rather than removing it.

customer value An aspect of a product or service for which a customer is willing to pay.

cycle time The time it takes to successfully complete the tasks required for a work process.

defect A part, product, or service that does not conform to specifications or a customer's expectations. Defects are caused by errors.

demand-supply chain All the parts, materials, and services supplied by outside sources that are necessary to produce a product or service.

DTD (dock-to-dock) A metric that measures how long it takes raw materials or sub-components coming into a plant to be turned into finished products.

end-of-the-line inspection An inspection or check done at the end of a process. See also *judgment inspection.*

enterprise resource planning (ERP) The integration of all an organization's departments and functions onto a single computer system that can serve all those different departments' needs.

error Any deviation from a specified manufacturing or business process. Errors cause defects in products or services.

error-proofing devices Mechanical, electrical, or pneumatic devices that signal existing errors or prevent potential ones.

external processes Activities that an equipment operator can perform while the production line is still running. Compare to *internal processes.*

FIFO (first-in, first-out) A production method in which the oldest remaining items in a batch are the first to move forward in the production process.

5S's (Sort, Shine, Set in Order, Standardize, and Sustain) A method of creating a clean and orderly workplace that exposes waste and errors.

fixed costs Costs that aren't changed by production or service/sales levels, such as rent, property tax, insurance, and interest expenses. They are the costs of being in business. Compare to *variable costs.*

fixed-value method An error-proofing method that ensures the right quantity of parts is used or the right number of activities are performed.

FTT (first time through) A metric that measures the percentage of units or aspects of a service that are completed without error the first time they go through your work processes.

---

hard-cost savings Money that actually produces cash savings or profit increases and directly affects a company's profit-and-loss statement. Compare to *soft-cost savings*.

informative inspections An error-proofing method that provides timely information about a defect so that a root-cause analysis can be performed and process adjustments can be made before significant numbers of defects are created.

internal processes Activities that an equipment operator must perform while the production line is idle. Compare to *external processes*.

inventory Any part or product that is not immediately required for a customer order, such as excess raw materials, work in progress (WIP), and finished goods.

ITO (inventory turnover rate) A metric that measures how quickly your company sells the products you produce.

judgment inspection An error-proofing method in which a quality inspector or operator compares the final product or part with a standard. It is a type of end-of-the-line inspection.

just-in-time inventory (JIT) A method of inventory management in which small shipments of stock are delivered as soon as they are needed. JIT minimizes stocking levels.

kanban system A production-control system that uses cards or tickets as visual signals to trigger or control the flow of materials or parts during the manufacturing process.

lead time The time it takes to complete an activity from start to finish; it includes batch and process delays.

lean metrics Financial, behavioral, and core-process measurements that help you monitor your organization's progress toward achieving the goals of your lean initiative.

load balancing Finding a balance between the volume of work that your organization needs to do and your capacity.

load leveling Adjusting a production schedule to meet unexpected changes in customer demand.

location indicators Markers that show where and how much material should be kept in a specific location in a work area.

marketplace An area where materials are stocked in a supermarket system.

motion-step method An error-proofing method that involves checking to make sure actions are performed in the correct sequence.

OEE (overall equipment effectiveness) A metric that measures the availability, performance efficiency, and quality rate of your equipment.

OFLT (order-fulfillment lead time) The average time that elapses between your company's receipt of an order from a customer and when you send an invoice to your customer for the finished product or service.

one-piece flow The movement of products through the manufacturing process one unit at a time. Compare to *batch processing*.

OTD (on-time delivery) A metric that measures the percentage of units you produce that meet your customers' deadlines.

---

planned maintenance Maintenance activities that are performed on a set schedule. Compare to *reactive maintenance*.

PQ analysis table A tool that helps employees understand the types of products your organization produces and the volume that your customers demand. (The *P* in *PQ* stands for *products*; the *Q* stands for *quantity* of production output.)

process A series of steps or actions that produces a completed order or product.

process capacity table A tool for gathering information about the sequence of operations that make up a work process and the time required to complete each operation.

process delay The time that batches or lots must wait until the next process begins.

process route table A tool that shows the machines and equipment that are needed for processing a component or completing an assembly process. Aids in grouping your manufacturing tasks into work cells.

production smoothing Synchronizing the production of your company's different products to match your customer demand.

productivity The ratio of output to input. It provides information about the efficiency of your core processes.

pull system A production system in which goods are built only when requested by a downstream process. A customer's order "pulls" a product from the production system. Nothing is produced until it is needed or wanted downstream. Compare to *push system*.

push system A production system in which goods are produced and handed off to a downstream process, where they are stored until needed. This type of system creates excess inventory. Compare to *pull system*.

quality function deployment A structured process that provides a means to identify and carry customer requirements through each stage of product and service development and implementation. Quality responsibilities are effectively deployed to any needed activity within a company to ensure that appropriate quality is achieved.

quick changeover A method of analyzing your organization's manufacturing processes and then reducing the materials, skilled resources, and time needed for equipment setup, including the exchange of tools and dies. It allows your organization to implement small-batch production or one-piece flow in a cost-effective manner. ·

reactive maintenance Maintenance activities that are performed after a piece of equipment breaks. Compare to *planned maintenance*.

red-flag condition A situation in which the probability that errors will happen is high.

return on investment (ROI) Profit from an investment as a percentage of the amount invested.

root-cause analysis A process of identifying problems in an organization, finding their causes, and creating the best solutions to keep them from happening again.

RTY (rolled throughput yield) A metric that measures the probability that a process will be completed without a defect occurring.

self-inspection An inspection performed by the operator at his or her own workstation or area.

shadow board A visual control technique that uses an image of an object to show where it should be stored.

soft-cost savings Assets that are freed up so they can be used for another purpose. This contributes no positive change to a company's profit-and-loss statement. Compare to *hard-cost savings*.

source inspection An inspection that detects errors in the manufacturing process before a defect occurs in the final part or product.

standard operating procedures (SOPs) Reliable instructions that describe the correct and most effective way to get a work process done.

standard operations The most efficient work combination that an organization can put together.

standard operations combination chart A tool that enables you to study the work sequence for all your organization's work processes.

statistical process control (SPC) The use of mathematics and statistical measurements to solve an organization's problems and build quality into its products and services.

streamline To reduce the time spent in non-value-added steps, such as downtime, travel time, and inspecting or reworking materials.

successive inspection An inspection that is performed after one operation in the production process is completed, by employees who perform the next operation in the process.

supermarket system A stocking system in which materials are stored by the operation that produces them until they are retrieved by the operation that needs them. When a store is full, production stops.

symmetry When opposite sides of a part, tool, material, or fixture are, or seem to be, identical. The identical sides of a symmetrical object can be confused during an operation, resulting in errors. Compare to *asymmetry*.

takt time The total available work time per day (or shift) divided by customer-demand requirements per day (or shift). Takt time sets the pace of production to match the rate of customer demand. For example, if your customers demand 480 spark plugs per day and your production line operates 960 minutes per day, takt time is two minutes; if customers want two new contracts written per month, takt time is two weeks.

total productive maintenance (TPM) A series of methods that ensures every piece of equipment in a production process is always able to perform its required tasks so that production is never interrupted.

Traditional Cost Accounting (TCA) An accounting technique that arbitrarily allocates overhead to the products or services an organization creates. It is unable to calculate the actual cost of a product or service. Compare to *Activity-Based Costing (ABC)*.

value-added activities Tasks performed during the production of a product or service that increase its value to the customer.

value stream All the activities that a company must do to design, order, produce, and deliver its products or services to customers.

value stream map An illustration that uses simple graphics or icons to show the sequence and movement of information, materials, and actions in a company's value stream.

VA/NVA (value-added to non-value-added) ratio A metric that compares the amount of time in your work process spent on value-added activities to the amount of time spent on non-value-added activities.

variable costs Costs that vary with production or service/sales levels, such as the costs of raw materials used in the manufacturing process. Compare to *fixed costs.*

waste Any activity that takes time, resources, or space, but does not add value to a product or service.

work combination A mixture of people, processes, materials, and technology that comes together to enable the completion of a work process.

workflow The steps and motions employees take to perform their work tasks.

workflow diagram A graphic that shows your organization's current equipment layout and the movement of materials and workers during work processes.

work sequence The sequential order in which tasks that make up a work process are performed.

Notes

Notes

Notes

Notes